MONTAGUE MENDICK

THE QUANTUM SECRET OF LIFE

HOUSE OF KNOWLEDGE PUBLISHING
POWIS SQUARE, LONDON, W11 2AZ

Copyright © 2003 House of Knowledge Publishing

First Published 2003

Published by
House of Knowledge Publishing
19 Powis Square
London W11 2AZ

Printed in Great Britain

ACKNOWLEDGEMENTS

I would like to thank Stephon Alexander for his creative outlook and encouragement, Simone Grant for her steadfast support and assistance, Ioannis Raptis for his helpful criticism, Phil Jacobs for his views on science, Negar Esfandiary for her patience and professionalism, Terry Pilling for his editorial suggestions and our long, stimulating arguments on the profound questions of science, Tariq Bedeau for inspiring the publication of my ideas and my publisher Ishmahil Blagrove Jr for making this book possible.

CONTENTS

EDITOR'S PREFACE

Can knowledge of the structure of the universe be discovered by reasoning alone? This question has been posed by philosophers centuries ago. Since then, many scientists tend to believe that the universe and its laws are independent of human rationality and independent of the minds that are discovering them. This has not ended the hope that one can discover reality and the structure of the universe without recourse to anything outside of the human mind. The advent of ultra-modern physics has caused scientists to once again rely purely on thought and mathematical consistency to guide them into the exotic realms of possible realities. This book presents a new method of logic that attempts to understand the structure of nature via rational thought with a minimum of prior axioms.

Some of the biggest questions that we, as human beings, are deeply concerned with, such as how life originated, what is consciousness, what might be the point of it all and even whether there is a point, are questions that are seldom investigated by contemporary scientists. This is not because contemporary science cannot attempt to answer to these questions, but merely because our theories become more and more uncertain the further afield one applies the fundamental principles. But what if we do take the step? What if we apply the laws to their furthest limits and see where they lead? Although contemporary physics has tended to avoid this diversion this has not always been the case.

In the history of science right up until the early years of the 20th century, scientists have routinely crossed the line between the empirical and the philosophical. Great scientific minds of the past routinely delved into the philosophical implications of their work. In fact, it was this aspect of their work which has most often captured the attention of the general public. Unfortunately, with respect to these all encompassing philosophical questions, contemporary science seems to be barred by an invisible signpost declaring in the fashion of Dante': `All

1

hope abandon, ye who enter here.'

Recently, this has begun to change. Prominent scientists throughout the world are beginning to write books and articles which attempt to tackle questions beyond those within the traditional realm of physics. For example, Stephen Weinberg discusses the origin of the universe in *The first three minutes*. A famous paper by Freeman Dyson, [*Time without end: Physics and biology in an open universe*, Freeman J. Dyson, Rev. Mod. Phys, 51, 3 (1979).] discusses human life, hope and survival in the far future of our universe. More recently, Roger Penrose has written books (*The Emperor's New Mind* and *Shadows of the Mind*) about consciousness and postulates how it may be understood in terms of underlying physical principles and biological structures. These scientists are the pathfinders. They are insisting that the lines between the empirical and the philosophical are not barriers to be feared but rather ethereal obstacles which should be explored from both sides.

In the present book, Mr. Mendick tackles many of these deep metaphysical questions from the viewpoint of logic and consistency. He points out weaknesses of our modern fundamental theories of nature and suggests his own solutions to these weaknesses. This work is a presentation of the logical, metaphysical and philosophical foundations of a new scientific theory of nature. It is also a discussion of modern physics with an emphasis on the aspects which are inconsistent with our inherent notion of continuity and reality. He asks whether equations and theories which break down in certain limits should be trusted to reveal truth, he then proceeds to outline a completely different structure for a physical theory. A different philosophical foundation upon which science should rest, intended to overcome many of the paradoxical dilemmas of the conventional philosophy. He uses his ideas of C, P and T violation as the backdrop enabling him to weave a path through the history of logic, philosophy, linguistics, biology, genetics and physics.

Centuries ago, empirical measurement began to displace the philosophical conjectures of the ancients as a means for discovering truth in nature and, since then, scientists, pleased with the apparent ability of measurement to reveal absolute truth, have begun to discredit philosophical inquiry as being an unworthy pursuit. The huge advances in microscope, telescope, electronic and particle accelerator technology of the 20th century has caused physicists to further condemn those who dare to bring the undulating ocean of philosophy onto the hard factual rock of physics. The attitude in many cases is that speculation about the unmeasurable ``truth'' underlying science is unworthy of investigation by legitimate scientists. I believe that this attitude is unhealthy. All forms of investigation should be happily pursued and should not be condemned.

The investigations of Mr. Mendick begin on firm empirical ground with the experimental discovery of CP violation in the decay of neutral kaons. Given that CPT must be conserved in any quantum theory, this implies that we must also have T violation. Mendick argues that violation of time reversal at a microscopic level is exactly what is needed to explain macroscopic time reversal asymmetry as embodied in the second law of thermodynamics. He then steps back and declares that if CP and T are violated in neutral kaon decay, we should take it a step further and examine the implications of discarding CPT as a fundamental symmetry of our theory. This would mean that quantum theory itself is incomplete since it can not cope with such a violation. Thus, using the non-conservation of CPT as the fundamental starting point, he proceeds to construct a theory of nature which takes this into account from the start. He does not construct the theory in a rigorous mathematical sense, but in a logical sense. He outlines what a unified theory must contain in order that it be consistent with the violation of CPT, he constructs a collection of axioms as a base for his new logical system and then he follows where it leads, first in resolving various paradoxes and then tackling some of the big questions of science. Interestingly, his investigations lead to answers to some very deep questions if boldly carried to classical regimes. In fact, he confidently applies the principle to all scales stating that violation at small scale (say particles) implies violation at the next scale up (say atoms) and so on. This leads to a vast range of conjectures from the origin of entropy to even the origin of life!

There are several differences between my views of physics and those of Mr. Mendick. The main difference is that he believes that a theory of the universe need not be stated mathematically and that our philosophical ideas are more fundamental. I believe that one can only retain confidence in deductions when they are made mathematically. For example, there are many philosophical interpretions of a given wavefunction, but there is only one mathematical expression for it. Logical deductions from the interpretation are, in my opinion, less acceptable than mathematical deductions made from the equation. With respect to particle physics, he holds the controversial viewpoint that there are only two forces of nature - the electromagnetic and the gravitational and that the neutrino is responsible for gravity. He takes a very anthropomorphic viewpoint of the universe deducing from his theory that the evolution of the universe necessitates the evolving of human conciousness. He defines the concept of `knowability' as being the cause of the collapse of the quantum wavefunction from a superposition of states to a unique eigenstate. Since knowability requires a mind, he deduces that human consciousness is inevitable and follows from the logical laws of the universe. I find it difficult to agree with this point of view, but I find it very interesting nontheless.

Even with these differences there are many aspects of his views that I share. I enjoyed reading his book and I believe that everyone, scientist and non-scientist alike will enjoy it as well. His sense of humor, his knowledge of the history of the sciences and his ability to expose the philosophical weaknesses in our current theoretical understanding of nature is a very pleasurable mix. Even if you disagree with his premises or his deductions (as I do in a number of cases) you will still find it a fascinating intellectual trek through the sciences.

Terry Pilling Phd
London, 2003

Lucky is he who has been able to understand the causes of things
Virgil

1

INTRODUCTION

It was thought, until the nineteenth century, that life could originate almost anywhere. In Darwinian theory it seems more likely that life originated purely by remote chance, just once. Darwin thought that the pursuit of the origin of life was sheer fantasy. In the twentieth century, with the discovery of the structure of protein and nucleic acid, opinion has veered more to the opinion of the past, that life can originate anywhere, given the right conditions, according to strictly deterministic laws. This view appeared to receive support from the Miller experiment of 1953, which easily produced amino acids, the building blocks of protein, from simpler constituents. The idea was pursued vigorously by Stuart Kauffman. He maintained that his computer analogue experiments revealed that any system, regardless of its constituents, would, at some critical level of complexity, self-organise and not descend into chaos as you would expect, producing as a result, emergent qualities obeying deterministic, computable laws (algorithms). The implication is that life originated in a self-organising system, "at the edge of chaos", and proceeded to evolve deterministically, to higher levels of hierarchical organisation. Though severely flawed, this is a forthright, down to earth, practical approach, which contrasts favourably with the weaving of statistical fantasy, in a never-never land of jingoistic idolatry and just-so histories, now the hallmark of neo-Darwinist "explanation". Biologists—John Maynard Smith for example—have dismissed the Kauffman hypothesis as nonsense. They would, wouldn't they? Biologists, palaeontologists, ethologists, zoologists and anthropologists will have no truck with physics encroaching on their domain. Physics is deemed by Darwinists as being unable to explain biology or man as clinging to an outworn, essentialist Aristotelian philosophy, contradicted by the species concept (the species concept in Darwinism is self-contradictory if evolution is continuous). Kauffman's hypothesis has the merit of being a physical (as distinct from a solely chemical-biological) hypothesis, of being integrative (systemic, nonreductionist) and above all, of having an emphasis on a principle of self-organisation. It also goes where (almost) no scientist has gone before (he was preceded by I. Prigogine) in trying to solve a problem which Bohr said—in the context of the analogous problem of the origin of mind—was insoluble in principle. Physicists had come to expect having the door slammed in their face by the biologists, who gave the philosophy of the *whole* of science, and even of morality, a Darwinian focus, emphasis and reinterpretation. This focus, like that of physics, was contingent, acausal and nondeterministic, so physicists were slain by their own sword. But over the last decade book after book has appeared maintaining that quantum theory, if correctly formulated, must be able to explain life. (It's not physics which is at fault but physicists, in that they have the wrong quantum philosophy). What, then, are the problems which a quantum theory of the origin of life must answer if it is to explain the existence of life in the universe?

The question naively assumes that we know what matter is but have yet to find out what life is. But our ramshackle, makeshift quantum theory, an unconvincing, tottering contraption of the 1920's, cannot explain matter let alone life. So let's turn the problem on its head. Let a quantum theory of life throw light on a quantum theory of matter by a continually evolving the process of interaction, each theory emerging from the other as a consequence. Let quantum theory, in short, evolve *like life itself*. By this means there will evolve a new general relativistic quantum theory as the basis of *all* scientific theory (physics, biology, psychology, logic, linguistics and mathematics.) This seems inordinately ambitious, perhaps frighteningly so, but the course of cultural evolution demands, with clear and unmistakable signals, that this be done *now*. Paul Davies, with prophetic judgement, writes, "The nature of reality, of time, space, mind and matter, will suffer a revolution of unprecedented profundity..." The unification must of course include the force of gravity, which many current theories have failed to do.

The quantum problems of the origin of life are: What are the molecular interactions in a prebiotic system which ensure it evolves deterministically, to produce life? How are invariant molecular structures produced in a living cell? Does the system begin with macromolecules or do they evolve from ordinary-sized molecules? At what stage are the enormous discontinuously larger supramacromolecules produced, and by what mechanism; (in the nonliving world there are no such molecules and all attempts to make them in the laboratory have failed)? How do the structures of a prebiotic system evolve such as to produce functionality, which only life possesses? Are there new laws of physics involved, or is it just a question of familiar parts being differently arranged? What are the laws obeyed by the prebiotic macrosystem? What are the *macro* laws of the biotic system, and how do they *relate* to the *micro*-interactional laws?

The perennially vexing Descartes ontological question, "Has life a separate reality?" must be answered with a new logical system. Nothing less than a revolution in logic is essential. The theory must answer the question, "What is the true nature of process?"—living and non-living—since life (as will be proven) is a one-way process. The living process must throw light on the non-living.

The EPR (Einstein-Podolsky-Rosen) paradox today enjoys a notoriety because of nonlocality not dissimilar to that of absolute space a century ago. Both are linked to key experiments (the Michelson-Morley and the Aspect experiment respectively). Its resolution is essential to an understanding of the crucial final stage in the origin of life when function makes its entrance on the evolutionary scene for the first time in the universe. The answer to this question is astonishing. Einstein is seen to be justified in attempting to define reality. The vital clue to the origin, silently screaming at us, is that all amino acids of living systems are L-handed enantiomers (are left handed) and all pentose sugars in nucleotides are R-handed (are right handed). The great biochemist Louis Pasteur, way ahead of his time, discovered, in the 1860's, that most of the organic substances of living things are handed. Whereas, since particle physics did not exist, he saw no such handedness in non-living things. He even proposed, nevertheless, that the entire universe is asymmetrical in construction. An unbiased physicalist interpretation of this suggests that interactions, which violate the discrete symmetries of C, P, and T, are dominant in living systems. But in view of what was said earlier about the top-bottom relationship, it must now be assumed, despite appearances, that they are also dominant in non-living matter. The emphasis in the physics of both living and non-living systems must be on the concepts of organisation, asymmetry, nonlinearity, and real (not just virtual) non-conservation of energy and momentum. In thermodynamics, in the equilibrium state of an isolated system, there is a balance of non-conserved energy, so that energy is conserved. Consequently, natural disasters such as the dissipation of systems, do not happen. We logically require that science be explanatory (and not merely descriptive). So causality is defined as a logically asymmetric relation of necessary implication (a relation of implication which is an ordered pair). This resolves the mathematical paradox of material implication, which fails to convey the intuitive meaning of the conditional. In agreement with the profound philosophy of Einstein and Bohm (as opposed to the absurd and unsatisfying "solipsistic" philosophy of Bohr and Heisenberg), it is necessary to provide a new ontology for science. It is now obligatory to define the concepts of: reality, truth, energy, mass, charge, entropy, work, heat, organisation, life, gene, mutation, experience, feeling, consciousness, wave-function, particle, atom, molecule, (macro and supramacromolecule), causality, word, meaning and concept.

A unified theory of science must resolve certain outstanding problems, some of contemporary science, but even going as far back as Newton. A contemporary problem is that of "the infinities", one already present in classical physics: as a charge shrinks to a point, the inverse square law of electromagnetic force yields infinite values of force and inadmissible infinite values of energy. The same problem has appeared in quantum theory. In the present theory there cannot be energy distributed over a point, so no such infinities can arise. In Newtonian theory the inertial force is unexplained; a new theory must explain this. There must be no evading this, no talk of fictional force (only of real force) or of a vacuum with implied miraculous properties. The central pillar of classical physics, the second law of thermodynamics, remains as solitary and inscrutable as ever. The basic problem of the second law of thermodynamics, how a one-way process can be the logical outcome of purely time-symmetric interactions, has not yet been resolved. This problem, no matter how much sophistry is forced upon it, will simply not go away. It is solved, in our theory, by giving it a fundamentally new approach, which redefines entropy in terms of organisation (not chaos), and explains the microscopic one way increase in terms of T violating asymmetric interactions. Macro-asymmetry can only be explained by micro-asymmetry. Because it is a theory solely of symmetry, the Einstein general theory of relativity—for long a bulwark of physics—must be abandoned, great theory though it is.

Quantum theory, on its own, fares no better than relativity. Relativity may pretend that it can ignore, or discount, the clock paradox but quantum theory, like mathematics and logic, is besieged by a welter of paradoxes, beginning with Schrodinger's cat which purrs as enigmatically as ever. Those few brave physicists who have attempted to stroke this strange cat have had their fingers bitten! In Neumann's theory an act of consciousness collapses the wavefunction and, inadvertently, also collapses its credibility. This falsely implies that no reduction occurs, prior to human presence in the universe. (The philosophical dilemma of George Berkeley strikes again: it has come home to roost, kicking and screaming, in quantum theory). The root of the dilemma is this: if you, most reasonably posit reduction, you must—to be consistent—posit a *cause* for the reduction. But quantum theory seems to deny the existence of causality in physics. The same fundamental problem, the search for a cause, in a seemingly causeless world, is evident in the second law of thermodynamics; there is no causality in a world ruled by the roll of the dice. (Einstein thought that god never plays dice; quantum theory is thought to say that God only plays dice.) As the present theory proves, this version of quantum theory, mad though it appears, takes a decisive step towards the truth. You don't have to be mad in science, but it helps. Bohm's theory is also realist but there is no reduction, no real logical foundation; it leans heavily towards an eastern mystical form of holism, full of eastern promise, which is entirely lacking in conviction. The incomparably successful and great tradition of western scientific culture, of which we should be proud, needs radical extension, not substitution. In the face of the intimidating challenge of the science of life, scientists must not suffer a loss of nerve and resort to spurious solutions or makeshift philosophy. The scientific quest is now as much a search for the answers to life, as for the structure of matter in the universe. We must reject the reactionary stance of so many biologists, with their nonsensical concepts of "selfish genes" and "memes" and their hostile attitude towards a new biology which must be based on a scientific understanding of consciousness and experience.

Darwinist theory correctly deduces that there must be favourable mutations (variations). It makes only a negative statement as to their cause: they are not caused by the development (the behaviour, morphogenesis or needs) of the organism. They might—since Darwin does not prove otherwise—even be the result of Providence or god, which god forbid. It says they arise purely by chance, but not in the physicists' sense of the word, which is that a chance event is one which *in principle* has no cause. So what the theory is really saying is that a favourable mutation has an unknown cause and that a certain kind of cause is proscribed. But if it is unknown, this is logically an admission that the cause could be development after all. We deduce within our logical system that this is so.

Physicists and biologists do not yet understand that Godel's theorem is indispensable to the evolution of all science. For those unacquainted with Godel's theorem, the following comments will prove helpful. The great mathematician David Hilbert, at the turn of the twentieth century, disturbed by the proliferation of paradoxes in mathematics, accumulated over a few centuries, resolved to clean up the house of mathematics by introducing a formalist philosophy of mathematics. Mathematics must above all be consistent. Hilbert felt that it should be possible to formalise all of mathematics, and to find a finite proof of the consistency of mathematics. The project was known as Hilbert's Programme. The great logician, Kurt Godel dealt this ambition a death blow. In 1931 his first incompleteness theorem proved that no finite, formal, consistent axiomatic system can correctly answer all questions about the addition and multiplication of numbers. There are always undecidable propositions which can be proved neither true nor false. A theory of whole numbers, if consistent, must also be incomplete. Any such axiomatic system is incomplete. There are always true statements, which a system can express but cannot prove, though they can be proved by a stronger system. He also proved, as a corollary, that any system, rich enough to embrace whole numbers, cannot prove its own consistency. This is known as his second incompleteness theorem. From the first theorem, if a system is complete, it must be inconsistent. If truth is to be defined within an axiomatic system it must contain an undecidable proposition. Within mathematical language we can only assert that a proposition is deductively valid, not that it is true, because we cannot know whether our assumptions are true. To say that a valid deduction is true is to make a philosophical, not a scientific statement. When we say a proposition is true we have in mind that something really is so. This implies that the words 'really is' provide the answer to what is truth. This ontological question cannot be answered within mathematical language. We shall see that Godel's theorem leads to the definition of truth by relating it to the universe and logically assuming that Kant's postulate that existence is not a predicate is false.

The Violation of the The Three
Discrete Symetries of C, P, T

There is a well-known correspondence between invariance under transformations and conservation laws (Noether's theorem). For example, invariance of a physical system under spatial translation leads to conservation of linear momentum; invariance under rotation leads to conservation of angular momentum; invariance under time evolution leads to conservation of energy, and so on. Each of these transformations is *continuous*.

There are also three *discrete* symmetry transformations: a parity (P) operation; a charge (C) operation; a time-reversal (T) operation. These, too, lead to conservation laws. The image of a person in a mirror is an incomplete parity operation since only the z-coordinate perpendicular to the mirror is reversed, whereas P requires reversal of all the coordinates (x to -x, y to -y and z to -z). If your mirror image could speak it would say (on reflection) that it has a left hand and a right hand, combs its hair and so on. So the world is physically unchanged after this parity transformation. So we say parity (P) is conserved and this is a new conservation law. Right and left, up and down, forward and backward in time were always thought to be physically indistinguishable because Newton's and Maxwell's laws are invariant under P and T. The contradictory nature of the macroscopic one-way directionality in time of the second law of thermodynamics was either regarded as an inexplicable anomaly, or explained away as not really being a law of necessity but merely a contingent statistical effect of large numbers, a most probable state being produced, but not of necessity, from T conserving interactions; that is, interactions which do not violate T. The correct interpretation of this lies at the heart of the new physics. A P operation on a system of interacting particles means to replace that system with its mirror image. It is a spatial inversion operation, which has the effect of changing left-handed particles to right-handed ones and vice versa. P violation occurs when the rate of a particle interaction is different to the mirror image of that interaction. If interaction forces have the same strength for left-handed and right-handed particles, then the parity operation is symmetrical for these interactions. Parity is conserved by them. Parity is violated if the mirror image is distinguishable from the imaged system.

The weak nuclear interaction—the radioactive beta-decay process—has been found to be asymmetric for right-handed and left-handed particles and thus violates P symmetry. C. S. Wu and her collaborators found that when a cobalt-60 nucleus was placed in an electrromagnetic field, electrons from the decay were preferentially emitted in a direction opposite to that of the aligned angular momentum of the nucleus. When it is possible to distinguish these two cases in a mirror, parity is not conserved. Before this experiment it was thought that the world showed no preference for left or right. In a weak interaction nature herself, by her own intrinsic handedness, has provided an operational definition of left and right. The experiment could be used to communicate to extraterrestrials what we mean by left and right, by means of a law of microphysics alone, and without any reference to the obvious asymmetry of the objects of the macroworld. The world is basically handed, because it is handed at the microlevel. The world is asymmetrical in its construction. To what extent is the world handed? Is the world, nevertheless, almost entirely symmetrical, with weak interactions the odd exception to almost inviolable symmetry? Truth, maidenly discreet, always walks on tiptoe, when it's not screaming. Could this relatively meagre but real presence of asymmetry merely be the portent of the flood of asymmetry to come? To answer this we must see whether the world is handed for the other transformations, C and T.

Charge conjugation is a mathematical operation that transforms a particle into an anti-particle, for example changing the sign of the charge. It implies that every charged particle has an oppositely charged antimatter counterpart or antiparticle. For years it was assumed that charge conjugation and parity were exact symmetries of elementary processes, namely those involving electromagnetic, strong and weak interactions. The same was held to be true for time reversal (T) which corresponds to reversal of motion. Invariance under T implies that whenever a motion is allowed by the laws of physics, the reversed motion is an allowed one.

C. S. Wu and collaborators also showed in 1957 that charge conjugation symmetry is also separately broken during the weak interaction process of beta-decay. The discovery that the weak interaction conserves neither parity nor charge conjugation, separately led to a quantitative theory establishing *combined* CP as a symmetry of nature. So perhaps nature is predominantly symmetrical after all. It was assumed that the combined symmetry of CPT constituted an exact symmetry of all types of fundamental interactions. Physicists reasoned that, given the invariance of CPT, if CP is invariant T is also invariant. But further experiments carried out in 1964 by J. Cronin and V. Fitch, demonstrated that the electrically neutral K meson (kaon) which was thought to breakdown into three pi mesons, decayed, a fraction of the time, into only two such particles, thereby violating CP symmetry. If CPT is not violated, and CP is, then T is also violated. On currently accepted theory, P and C conservations are upheld by all the forces of nature, except the weak nuclear force. And even the weak nuclear force usually conserves the compound CP operation. In only one small corner of physics: the decay of K mesons, has CP violation been observed, although physicists suspect that CP violation must somehow operate on a large scale.

The famous CPT theorem states that it is almost impossible to write down a quantum theory that is consistent with special relativity which is not symmetric under the combined CPT operation. Believing something is so does not make it so. The house of discrete symmetries is considered to have three floors. The ground floor is CPT conservation. The second floor has collapsed because its separate symmetry rooms of C and P have been violated. The first floor, CP combined, is swaying, on the point of collapse, most would say it already has collapsed. It is time to vacate the premises! We postulate the violation of CPT. This postulate will of course seem completely crazy. Niels Bohr and Freeman Dyson said that any theory of the elementary particles which does not appear at first sight to be completely crazy cannot be correct. We humbly submit that our theory satisfies the rigorous scientific criterion of being sufficiently crazy to be the new unified theory of physics, for which we have been searching so long. The house of symmetry is falling about us; we must forge a new science from asymmetry. With this postulate, of CPT violation, we construct a theory of the evolution of the universe and a theory of the evolution of a prebiotic system, culminating in the specific laws governing the origin of life at the micro and macro-systemic levels. We shall demonstrate that the universe evolves according to laws, which obey a newly defined law of general relativity, with the formation of different hierarchical levels of organisation, from particle to atom to molecule, to life as a necessary consequence of the evolution of the violation of the discrete symmetries.

2

THE LOGICAL
LAWS OF ONTOLOGY

As an introduction to the Logical Laws of Ontology it is noted that for centuries, the main philosophical problem has been, What does knowledge consist of, and how do we construct it? Kant thought he had solved this problem. He thought there was empirical knowledge—true a posteriori—derived from sensory experience, this being real knowledge of the universe. No philosopher, empirical or rational, has ever been able to say precisely what this means. What is the relation between knowledge and sensory experience and how is it obtained? The difficulty is that knowledge requires a knower; the knower is a mind, but science does not know how to analyse the subjectivity of mind objectively. There is a clash, or so it would appear, between subjective and objective truth. Frege was a Platonist, he believed that abstract truths such as mathematical truths, have their own independent reality. With Frege's suspicion of the subjectivity of logic in linguistic theory and the fear that subjectivity had even entered the stronghold of the quintessentially, objective science of physics, with the non-invariant properties of special relativity, this clash intensified with ever increasing strength throughout the following century. The amorphous sea of troubles which swamped Descartes in his failed attempt to construct a theory of knowledge, was now beginning to assume a more solid shape. To reason deductively is to make a set of postulates and by assuming the existence of a logical law of implication, to deduce statements (conclusions) from the postulates. The logical difficulty with empirical philosophy is that it must deny deductive reasoning, since this requires knowledge of the law of implication, which cannot be known empirically. Empirical knowledge of this law is impossible since it cannot be reasoned from the senses (no "law" can be derived from the senses, only contigent knowledge). Empirical reasoning is possible but not *deductive* empirical reasoning. So the claim of empiricism that it can discover real knowledge of the universe as law (which we shall see later is *necessary* truth) is false. Empiricism can only non-deductively discover contingent truth, which (as we shall see later) is factual truth. Empriricism can only deduce contingent knowledge of the universe if it borrows the clothing of rationalism, that is, if it becomes rationalism.

Besides empirical knowledge, Kant also thought there was the a priori knowledge of analytic propositions. These were a priori because they required no examination of the universe to discover their truth. Their truth was necessary because considered self-evident, they were conventional truths resulting from linguistic definitions; if the definitions were true, the propositions were true. This being so, they had nothing new to say about the universe. These seemingly innocent truths turned out to be no less questionable than empirical truths. He called the latter synthetic a posteriori. This created a hotbed of controversy over the status and significance of innocent truths which raged ever more strongly into the twentieth century. The root of the controversy was that philosophers and logicians were finding it natural to think of analytic truths as truths of logic. Unlike the truths of classical logic, analytic truths were not form dependent but also depended on meaning. So, almost unawares, they were calling into question the validity of classical logic. There was a collateral growing realisation that classical logic had to be refined by the creation of symbolic logic and, if necessary, replaced or supplemented by other kinds of logic, for example modal logic. The barrier to doing this was that the most important law of the process of logical reasoning, the law of implication, could not be defined without contradiction. This law was taken to be the law of material implication, which led to the contradiction that a false proposition implied anything, true or false, thus casting a cloud over the validity of the entire activity of logical reasoning. With his assertion of empirical and analytic truths, Kant won the approval of the empiricists, but with a devastating third and final step, he set the cat of rationality among the empirical pigeons. Philosophy was never the same again. Aristotle had, at last, found a worthy successor, one who could meet the challenges of the future logic of science.

To reconcile rationalism with empiricism, Kant asserted that there are, in addition to empirical and analytic truths, synthetic a priori truths about the universe, which are necessarily true. These are not truths of logic, but are truths arrived at intuitively, arising from the way in which—as organisms with a certain mental and physical structure—we necessarily perceive the structure of the universe. He thought that it was only with such knowledge that we can discover empirical truth. Kant was an empiricist as well as a quasi-rationalist. He was wrong in thinking that the synthetic a priori are structural laws of the universe. They are laws of logic. Like so many scientists since, he confused logic with structural law. For this reason he did not fulfil his intention of giving the human mind primacy over the universe, a philosophical change of attitude of which he was justly proud. The human mind could not yet deduce the universe from an armchair, as Descartes hoped.

In the present theory, we introduce a revolution in logic: we postulate that there are laws of logic of a new kind in logical theory. They are defined as logical laws of the universe. They are distinct from logical laws of mathematical language, though there are logical laws which belong to both systems. Kant's intention was to create a revolution, by not regarding mind as the passive observer of the universe but, inversely, to make the universe responsive to mind. He thought logic was unable to discover what is new in the universe, but he thought this could be discovered by synthetic a priori which is *not* logic. Kant was wrong: the synthetic a priori, which he constructed in his categories, when correctly formulated, are laws of logic. He did not succeed in his revolution because he did not know how to relate experience to reality and confused structural and logical law. Those who were prepared to think of analytical propositions as logical propositions were not prepared to do so for synthetic propositions, since these do not arise solely from definitions. Some propositions, regarded as being analytical, do not in fact arise solely from definitions. Some analytic propositions, at least (as will be explained in the linguistic section), assume the existence of logical laws of the universe, which are not the logical laws of mathematical language.

It is an illusion (as we shall deduce within our logical system) to think the laws of universal structure can be discovered empirically. There is no such thing as an empirical law. All knowledge is obtained by reasoning. All animals with mind, monkeys for example, have the ability to reason, which produces the knowing of a set of contingently true invariant causal relations between known sensory experiences. (The invariance is under time translation). This set is a cognitive experience. They know the causal relation but not the causal law of implication which the relation obeys. Animals do not know laws, so their reasoning is not deductive. They know relations that are true, but not the truth of the relations. Contingent truth, which requires deduction, is that obtained by the assumption of a set of factual premises from which conclusions are deduced by the logical law of implication from the premises. The knowledge of facts requires the knowledge of laws of logic, for example, the laws of factual logic and the law of implication. Animals do not know facts since animals do not make propositions. Only man knows laws, so only man can reason deductively. Structural laws can only be formed by deductive reasoning. Science is produced by rationalism, never by empiricism, since the structural laws of the universe are deduced from the logical laws of the universe but never from sensory experience. Only facts, contingent truths, can be deduced from sensory experience. Empiricists claim that usually experiment has provided the answer long before theory has developed the question. All experiment is theory-saturated. No amount of empiricism can lead inevitably to the deduction of the concept of force, but once the mind, not the senses, has created this concept, then and only then is the mind directed to the vast possibilities of experimental observation. We must set up rational logical systems for the formation of deductive contingent and deductive necessary truth. It is necessary to postulate a set of logical laws of the universe, and to deduce from these universal structural laws. If the logic is true, and the logical law of universal implication (to be defined later) is true, the deduced structural laws will also be true. If the logic is false, no such deduction of laws is possible, only the deduction of contradictory propositions.

No law is self-evident. The laws of logic cannot be proven true (but can only be used to prove other laws true); so how do we know that they are true? This is the real nature of the problem of knowledge. The truth of the laws of logic can only be based on faith. Not religious faith, but scientific faith, since the laws of logic must contain laws which define truth and truth cannot be defined within the universal system. This must include faith in *defined* law of causal implication, which is used to deduce structural laws of the universe from the set of logical laws, which are logical laws of the universe. This kind of deduction is *defined* as *proof* and the structural laws are said to be *proven* by the system. Mathematicians are no better off than scientists in respect of proof. They assume the truth of unprovable postulates and make deductions of theorems from these using an *unprovable* law of implication, which, as we shall see, is acausal. The structural laws of the universe are deduced from the logical laws of the universe. When this is completed, logic is science and not philosophy. Philosophy is a statement of those attitudes which produce the laws of science. Logic is a statement of the scientific laws of thought. There are logical laws of mathematical language and logical laws of the universe.

Kurt Godel did not attempt to define truth, but assumed, philosophically, the existence of the concept. In 1931 he proved that all the truths of mathematics cannot be proven within the system of mathematics. This means that truth cannot be defined within mathematical language since there could exist some as yet unknown undecidable proposition which renders the entire system inconsistent. The consistency of mathematics is solely a matter of faith, but there is no purely mathematical concept that could justify such an act of faith. This can only be found outside the logically closed system of mathematical language. But mathematics is the language of science, so scientific truth likewise cannot be defined within the mathematical system of the universe. Philosophers have attempted to define truth by saying a proposition is true if it has a correspondence with the way things really are. But this produces circularity: how does one know the truth of an assertion about the way things really are? Einstein demonstrated how to resolve a circular paradox: you enter the circle by a postulate, and explore the consequences. Philosophers have at times thought of trying to define scientific truth in terms of an explicit reality, but without success. John Searle, the philosopher, has suggested doing so but did not pursue this further. The nature of the difficulty is first: How do you make science transcendental, by definition, without falling into the trap of religious mysticism? Second, the concept of such a reality is useless—as Schopenhauer, though not Kant realised—unless the mind can relate to it in a valid way. Only relate. To answer these questions, the ontological logical laws of the universe are formulated.

In this chapter we present the logical laws of ontology. These are the laws of existence. All of the statements made in the remainder of this book are deduced from *this system of logic*. We stress this in order to prevent possible confusion resulting from conflicting definitions used in everyday language. For example, when we use the term "fact", we *exclusively* mean the definition of "fact" given in postulate 12. This definition is *not* the same as either the dictionary definition of `fact' or the meaning as used conventionally by scientists or philosophers. We mean by "fact" a proposition which is *contingently* true, that is, one which although true, could have been otherwise in different circumstances. A similar statement applies to the use of the word "definition" which is defined in the linguistic section which follows. As opposed to contingency there is a logical law of *necessity*. A proposition which is necessarily true is defined as a "law". Under no circumstances can a "law" be false. Unconsciously, scientists and philosophers use the word "fact" (and the word "law" also) with a variety of different meanings and ambiguous philosophical interpretations, thus making the construction of a consistent logical system impossible.

In all logical systems there must exist a minimal number of undefined terms since otherwise one could explain almost anything by increasing the number of definitions to infinity. In the present logical system the terms selected as undefined are "thing", "relation", "exist" and "being". There is a set of things, there is a set of relations between things. There are different kinds of relations, for example, properties of things and processes which things undergo, for example, "exist" and `being' are relations of the latter kind.

The logical laws of ontology (of existence) are as follows:

1. All things exist.

2. There exists a relation called the law of hierarchy.

3. Things exist at different hierarchical levels. Absolute (ultimate) reality is defined as the only thing that can be said to be; all other things only exist (and cannot be said to be). Reality is defined in terms of the undefined con cepts.

4. A real thing, which is not absolute, is defined as one which symbolises reality; an unreal thing, as one which does not symbolise reality. For example, this book exists and symbolises reality, whereas a 6-headed rhinoceros exists in the mind but does not symbolise reality. The book is real and the rhinoceros is unreal.

5. Reality is one (singular) and undifferentiated (indivisi ble). It is the absolute or (ultimate) reality.

6. Absolute reality is unknowable. (There are no structural laws of reality, only logical laws.) Only a logical relation can be made between the mind and absolute reality.

7. There is a law of identification. A real thing is identified by a set of real properties. (A real property may be invariant (e.g. charge) or non-invariant (e.g. linear momentum) under GCT)

8. The universe is the set of all real things, which exist in space-time. There is only one universe. (The universe is a really existing thing but cannot be said to be). The uni verse is not absolute reality.

9. There are three continuous dimensions of space and one

continuous dimension of time. They are unified to form a universal four-dimensional space-time continuum (Einstein's law).

10. A proposition is true if it symbolises reality, false if it does not.

11. There exists a logical law of necessity and of contin gency.

12. A fact is a proposition which is contingently true.

13. A law is a proposition which is necessarily true.

14. There are propositions which are neither true nor false.

15. A proposition and its negation cannot both be true (law of non-contradiction).

16. The logical law of causality is a law of universal impli cation. It is defined as an ordered pair (A, B), ordered such that A implies B of necessity, but B does not imply A. A is the cause of B.

The laws will now be explained. Science evolves from religious experience, which teaches us to think, logically, about the universe. "God" is a logical concept, which must now be assimilated within the scientifically defined logical concept of reality. The third law is by far the most important of all, being the foundation of the whole of science. Reality is at the highest level of existence, being the unique thing which creates all other things, real or unreal: it alone has being, as well as existence, where the undefined concept of "being" indicates that reality is at the highest hierarchical level of existence. The "ex" meaning "out of" in the word "existence", implies that being is more fundamental than existence. The use of the concepts, being and existence, in science, must not be confused with the way these are used in speech. Being is a verb, not a noun. Reality is not a "being". Being is a mode of activity, not a thing. Reality is a thing. The paradox of the meaninglessness of the denial of existence is easily resolved. We should like to deny the existence of Pegasus but what are we then denying: if there is no Pegasus, what existing thing is there to which we (contradictorily!) deny existence? There is a logical existential trap of circularity, which is baffling. The resolution is that we are not denying existence to Pegasus: we grant it an unreal existence but deny it real existence; (postulate 4). Russell and Meinong were wary of attributing existence to imaginary entities. Meinong thought that they had being but not existence. This is the reverse of the truth: only reality can be said to be. There is no set of all things, since this is contrary to the laws of set theory. There is a set of all real things, the universe. Clearly, there can only be one set of all real things (any other set containing all real things would be an identical set). So there is only one universe and not many universes, as posited by Hugh Everett. To postulate many universes is to postulate a different set of logical laws. If there were many universes there would be many realities but there is only one. Kant was wrong in thinking of reality, the "noumenon", as being differentiated, but correct in regarding it as unknowable. If it were knowable, Godel's theorem indicates that our system of knowledge would be complete and therefore inconsistent. Our system is incomplete, because reality is unknowable, but how do we know it is consistent? We don't. No logical system, by Godel's theorem, can ever prove its own consistency. It is necessary to have belief, to have faith in consistency, otherwise science cannot progress. The structure of absolute reality, should such a structure exist, is unknowable in principle; we only relate to reality by our faith in the truth (defined in terms of faith) of the laws of logic which are the laws, not of universal structure, but of the thought process. The laws of logic are laws of the mind, obeyed by the thought process. In the creative process, mind precedes universe: the true study of science is man. Man, alone in the animal kingdom, is at the centre of the universe. The structural laws of the universe are deduced from the laws of logic of the mind of man.

Reality is the most important concept of science. Its definition, and the definition of truth which follows from it, mark the beginning of a new kind of science, a new level of scientific consciousness, one in which concepts are defined and the sciences are unified. Unlike Kant's unknowable reality, reality is singular, not differentiated. Like Kant's unknowable reality, it is impersonal. These assertions are logical, not structural, since reality is unknowable. Whereas, in Kant's philosophy, the phenomenal constructs of experience (vision, for example) cannot be logically related to unknowable reality, in our theory, they are logically related to reality and to the universe. The objects of sensory experience in Kant's system cannot be related directly to reality. They are mere appearances, whereas in the present system such objects symbolise reality and are real. Post-Kantian philosophers understood the importance of relating to reality. Schopenhauer agreed with this and also saw reality as being singular. The purpose of constructing this logic of the universe, which relates to reality, is not to discover the structure of reality, since this is impossible, but to discover the structure of the universe.

Kant justified religious faith by scientific reasoning, which kept science separate from religion. He attempted to separate the unknowable metaphysics of religious experience from knowable science; religion in one box, science in the other. To achieve this, he postulated a differentiated, unknowable (transcendental) reality which is unrelated to religious faith. We define faith as the belief in a transcendental reality. An unknowable personal god, in his philosophy, could be logically related to by faith. But an unknowable impersonal reality could not be related to experience. This postulate had the effect of making his aim unrealisable, since it made it impossible to define reality, scientific truth and knowledge. The synthetic a priori set out the conditions or categories, which made empirical experience possible. This was a major advance in philosophy since it was, in effect, the construction of a set of logical laws of the universe, from which the structural laws of the universe could be deduced. Kant thought that with his synthetic a priori he was intuitively constructing structural laws of the universe, whereas they can only be deduced from a set of logical laws of the universe. Spinoza, unlike Kant, does not separate god from an unknowable reality, which lies beyond experience: this god is an unknowable god, which can be approached by the mind of man by logical constructs. Einstein's conception of reality was in part similar to Kant since it seems he unconsciously believed in a transcendental reality and in part similar in a pantheistic sense to Spinoza, but he did not believe in a personal god. He was obliged, because of his opposition to the Bohr anti-realists, to define physical reality, but he would have seen no point in defining a transcendental reality, as the time was not yet ripe. The pioneering rationalist philosophical constructions of Descartes, Leibniz, Spinoza and especially Kant, paved the way for the rationalist, scientific physical constructions of Maxwell's statistical thermodynamics, Einstein's relativity theory, and Neumann's quantum theory. All of these theories are metaphysical, but none introduced the patiently waiting transcendental metaphysics of Kant's philosophy into physics. Western philosophy has always been afraid to introduce metaphysical concepts into science, though this fear has to some extent evaporated. This is done, in our theory, by introducing a defined, unknowable, singular reality as a unifying concept for the whole of science. Whereas in Kant's philosophy faith in god is justified by science divorced from transcendental reality, in our theory, science, inversely, is justified by the application of reason to faith in a logically defined transcendental reality. In Kant's philosophy, faith and science are separate. In our theory, faith and science are unified, faith being the ground from which science springs, the ground in which it has its root. Kant constructed the concept of a transcendental reality in order to separate science from religion, whereas its real function is to unify science and faith. Kant justified religious faith by science; our theory justifies science by faith in a metaphysical reality. Reality must be related, logically, to experience, otherwise it is null and void, in the formation of a theory of knowledge. Kant attempted to split physics from metaphysics. Our theory identifies physics, and science in general, with metaphysics. All science is metaphysical science. Scientific truth is defined metaphysically.

Humean empiricism is false. All knowledge is produced by reasoning. Scientific law cannot be produced by empirical induction. This can only produce statements, which have only a probability of being true, whereas a law of nature must be true of necessity. Laws and facts symbolise reality, so they are invariant under time translation. The relations of cognitive experience are invariant under time translation and symbolise reality. Scientific cognitive experience of the universe is deduced from a set of logical laws of the universe. The non-scientific knowledge of non-human animals is also produced by reasoning, but animals do not know the laws of logic, so their reasoning is non-deductive. They know causal relations but they do not know the law of causality which these relations obey.

Animals have minds and therefore think. A mind, in its relation towards an object is said to have intentionality. This "aboutness" is really just another word for the directivity of consciousness towards objects in the universe. All consciousness, whether or not mental (i.e. even feeling), has this directivity or intentionality. The animal mind like the human mind, obeys laws of intentionality, of desire, fear, hope, decision and so on. This creates the paradox that if the object of fear, desire, etc., does not exist then there is a relation between a mind, which exists, and an object which does not. The paradox is resolved by noting that the desire for an object which does not exist is really a desire for an object, which has an existence, but only an unreal existence. Do the golden mountain and the round square exist? Yes. Do they really exist? Weren't you listening? Didn't you hear me say yes. They really exist but they don't exist, really; that is, they have an unreal but not a real existence. The first "really" in the previous sentence is used as in speech, whereas the second use of the word is its use in scientific mathematical language. Note that "exist", contrary to Kant's philosophy, is a predicate and not a copula, (that is, not merely a meaningless relating word).

Only man knows laws, that is, necessary truth. Man originated with the knowledge of law. Only man knows the logical laws of intentionality and can introvert about those laws. In particular, he can introvert about the logical law of belief. This means that he can apply the logical laws of reasoning to belief, to produce a system of faith, that is a reasoned system of belief in which there is asserted the belief in a transcendental reality, one not apprehensible to experience. This is the foundation, for the human mind, not only for the deduction of necessary truth, but also for the deduction of consciously expressed contingent truth. Animals know contingently true relations, which they reason non-deductively and which they cannot express. Classical logic claims that while there are other kinds of reasoning, this is the only kind of logical reasoning. It claims to achieve this by relying not on the meaning of words but solely on form and a small number of logical constants, such as "and", "not", "but", "all", "if". This is analogous to the claim of physicists that thermodynamics can be explained entirely in terms of ideal reversible processes. Strip physical reality of everything that matters and concentrate on a few idealised systems and then declare this to be the whole of reality. Strip language of all that is meaningful and pretend that the logical process depends on the nothing, called form, that is left. Then throw in a few simple words which we suppose are not just words, but logical constructions. Logicians say this, but this is not what they do. When a dubiously introduced logical constant becomes inconstant, that is, they must have regard to the meaning of the word, they reason on regardless and still call it logical reasoning. This is often justified but it is not classical logic. The truth is that there is no such thing as reasoning according to form any more than there is a strictly reversible process. Surreptitiously or otherwise, we do take the meaning of the logical constants into account in our reasoning. Here is an example of what classical logic would not call logical thinking - in Kant's philosophy, it would be called an analytic proposition.

Object P is blue; therefore object P is not yellow.

Logicians feel that the validity of the argument arises from content not form. It depends on the meaning of the words, blue and yellow, so that other predicates such as square and heavy would not preserve validity. In the present theory, the reasoning is logical and, without mincing matters, is stated, overtly, to arise from the meaning of the words. We reason so:

The object P, which we assume to be real, is identified by a set of real properties. This is a logical law of the universe. The meaning of the word blue is that of a colour, which is a real object- identifying property. The colour, yellow, would identify a different object, since yellow is also a real colour property. Therefore object P is not yellow. The properties square and heavy could obviously belong to the same object, so the validity of the argument depends on the meaning of the words. It is a miracle that the human mind could ever have believed logic to be classical. Let's look at a well-known Aristotelian syllogism:

"All men are mortal, Socrates is a man, therefore Socrates is mortal". In general, "All P are Q, Z is a P, therefore Z is Q".

In classical logic, the validity of the reasoning is supposed to stem from the logical constant "all", and the invariance of form. Not so. The reasoning depends on the meaning of the word "all". Any word, which comes after the word "are", must be a property of man, because of the meaning of "all". So Socrates, being a man, must be mortal, that is, must be identified by the property of being mortal. This is a logical law of the universe, law 7. The reasoning has nothing to do with form. Logicians have a bee in their bonnet about form. Bees are liable to sting. The reason syllogisms don't work if "all" is replaced by "some" could hardly be simpler; it has a different meaning.

Ludwig Wittgenstein said that the identity law is trivial. The analogy to this logical law of mathematical language is the law of identification, which is a logical law of the universe. This law is not trivial, having many important applications. The law of identification, axiom 7, is analogous to the logical law of identity of mathematical language. It means that we know a real thing as being that unique particular thing, by identifying it with its unique set of properties. If a real thing does not have a unique set of properties, it is indistinguishable from other things with the same set. Real universal things, which are unknowable, nevertheless, have a set of properties. The human mind cannot know everything, even in principle, but we must not have the hubris to think that what is unknowable does not exist; what is true of reality is no less true of quantum properties, in the superposed state. A particle, in a superposed state, always has a precise, though unknowable position. Examples of real things in axiom 7, are visual objects such as rocks, fruit, clouds, chairs and so on, also non-sensory objects such as atoms, particles, experiences and lives. Real things do not necessarily exist in space, they may exist only in time. We shall see that experiences and lives exist only in time. To establish, logically, the reality of things which exist in time alone we need a non-sensory reality, but we also need it to establish, logically, the reality of things which exist in space. The preceding phrase refutes the claim of

empiricism to be justifying the existence of a spatially existing reality. Axiom 7 corresponds to the "substance" category of Kant's philosophy, which he wrongly believed to be a
structural law of the universe, instead of a logical law.

The universe consists of all things which exist in space-
time. It is defined in terms of the concept of wavefunction,
since real things are so defined. The concept of a wavefunction of the universe can only be defined in terms of interacting universes since otherwise reduction of the universal
wavefunction would not exist. There is here, a logical definitional circularity: universe → wavefunction → universe.
By Godel's law, this is contradictory. This contradicts the
assertion of astrophysicists that the world has a wavefunction.

Note the distinction between fact and law in laws 12 and
13. Facts are a lesser form of truth: they only describe the
contingent structure of the universe, whereas laws formulate its necessary structure. A fact could have been, or could
be otherwise, but a law cannot be otherwise. Some physicists confuse the two; biologists almost invariably do so.
Biologists sometimes say that Darwin's law of evolution is
a fact, meaning it is certainly true, as if its being a law did
not mean it was certainly true. So much for the value of scientific law, in Darwinist thought. Darwinists are nothing if
not consistent in their epistemology, consistently wrong,
that is. Laws are a higher, not lower, form of truth than fact.
In classical logic, facts are not logical statements. Since a fact
is defined in terms of truth it must be a logical statement. (A
fact is a proposition, which is contingently true). To illustrate the importance of law 13, let us ask if a statistical
explanation of the second law of thermodynamics is possible. The answer is no, since this implies that there is always
the chance that the second law could be violated by some
highly improbable distribution of energy states. But the law
is not contingently true, it is true of necessity; that is, no violation of the law is possible, under any circumstances, in
our logical system. The law is explained, microscopically,

by T violating interactions. It is deduced (proven) later that Newton's laws, when truly relativistically formulated, are necessarily true in spite of, for example, the inapplicability of the law in certain physical contexts. Mathematicians fear the concept of causality as an alien being, logicians are confused and bewildered by it but would like to make its acquaintance, physicists hate and detest it and would not be seen dead in its company. The concept of causality does not appear in the statement of any physical law.

It is a law of logic that there are laws, laws of logic being a particular case of such laws. It is also a law of logic that there are facts. Neither law nor fact is god given, though we have a regrettable tendency to treat them as though they were. They are creations of the human mind. A fact is a statement of truth. Since truth is a logical concept, a fact is a logical concept. Though the latter law is a statement about contingency, it is necessarily true since it is a law. Just as objective statements can be made about the subjective, so necessarily true statements can be made about the contingent. There is an influential school of philosophy which regards the concept of truth as redundant. It says that the proposition A: "The cat sat on the mat", has exactly the same meaning as the proposition B: "It is true that the cat sat on the mat". The meaning of A is unknown until the context is known, whereas the meaning of B is immediately understood. B unambiguously states a fact whereas A may or may not do so, depending on context. "The cat sat on the mat", thought Angus "so they say; well, I don't believe it. That cat was not in the habit of sitting on mats." In this thought A is postulated as a premise, which could be a fact, but, on consideration, its proposed factual status is rejected, as it is thought to be untrue. This proves that A and B do not, necessarily, have the same meaning. This confusion is just plain silly. Angus is not asking a question, he is making a declarative statement, as one does when musing. A thought does not symbolise reality, whereas a declarative statement, if true, does. He says, "I like potatoes", "What

nonsense - I like potatoes - I hate potatoes." "I like potatoes," here, clearly does not mean, "It is true that I like potatoes." A known fact may be proposed as a factual premise
but this is not the same as a premise not known to be a fact
being proposed as a factual premise. A known fact must
begin with the words, "It is true that" but the latter premise
cannot begin with these words, without further qualifica-
tion. To emphasise the point, suppose Lee Harvey Oswald
had not been murdered, but had chosen to represent himself in court. Imagine that the prosecutor began with the
proposition F, "Lee Harvey Oswald killed President John F.
Kennedy by shooting him from a floor of the book deposi-
tory." Logically, Oswald would be correct to challenge this
statement, since if it were merely an unsupported premise
of a logical set, it would be clearly be inadmissible as an
opening statement. Whereas if it were intended to convey a
fact, it would have, immediately, to be supported by incon-
trovertible evidence. If it is an unsupported premise then its
meaning is that it is postulated that F is a fact, but it is not,
then, stating that F is a fact. Since such evidence is seldom
produced in a court of law (especially when there is no
body!), the law has to protect itself with the phrase "beyond
reasonable doubt". This does not mean that there are no
facts. It means that, since fact is a logical concept, it is, ultimately, a matter of judgement whether or not a given
proposition is a fact. The judgement is made by twelve of
our equals. "Facts are chiels that winna ding", says the poet,
Robert Burns, but there may, nevertheless, be much dinging
as to whether a given proposition is a fact. Was the prosecutor stating a fact? Opinion is divided. But either it is, or is
not, objectively, a fact. This demonstrates that the opening
proposition is different from the proposition, "It is true that
Lee Harvey Oswald killed...depository", since this is a
statement of fact. The latter symbolises reality, whereas the
former does not.

Law 14 is a denial of the truth of the law of bivalence as
a logical law of the universe. There are propositions that are

purely subjective, which are neither true nor false. "Mr. Smith is rich". Some may judge him rich, others not. A pauper may think him rich, a millionaire may think him poor. It depends on what one means by rich and by what principles you evaluate his means. The statement is neither true nor false. An unequivocal judgment presupposes an unequivocal criterion but there is none. The judgment is purely subjective. This does not mean that the law of bivalence is false. It is true, contrary to the belief of many mathematicians, for mathematical language, but is not true for universal propositions. Mathematicians fail to distinguish between the mathematical propositions of mathematical language and the mathematical propositions of the universe. The specification of the context is all-important. Mathematicians do not understand the difference between the truth of a geometrical law of mathematical language and the truth of a law of the geometrical structure of the universe. They have the false belief that the geometry of the universe is entirely a matter of empirical discovery, whereas it can only be arrived at by rational deduction, deduced from mathematical logical laws of the universe. The geometry of mathematical language is deduced from the logical laws of mathematical language, not from the logical laws of the universe. A law is necessarily true. Any real law, which does not appear to be true, is either wrongly or inadequately expressed. Newton's laws, as we shall see, when expressed quantum-relativistically are all real laws of nature. These laws have never been given a relativistically covariant formulation. Law 16 is discussed later in relation to the logical paradoxes.

An understanding of axiom 17, which states the law of causality, gives a most profound insight into the nature and magnitude of the proposed revolution in logic. David Hume thought that causality did not exist in the universe but was merely an ingrained habit of thought, while Kant thought that causality really existed and appeared necessarily to exist in the universe, because we are so constituted, mentally and physically, as to perceive its existence. The latter is much nearer the truth, because, in our system, causality is a logical law of the universe though there is some truth in both points of view. We do indeed *think* causally as Hume asserts, but we only do so because there is causality in the universe; we find the true nature of causality in the universe by making the correct premise of the logical law of causality. To understand the universe we must understand ourselves, the laws of our thinking process. The proper study of science is man. Kant created a purely *philosophical* reversal of attitude towards the relation between mind and universe, but failed to place the *logic* of the human mind at the centre of the universe. So he could not, causally, deduce the structural laws of the universe from its logical laws. He separated religion, based on faith, from science based on reason, in order to justify faith. But science must now assimilate religion, science itself being based on faith, a faith justified inversely by reason. This further inversion is an extension, not a contradiction of Kantian philosophy. Science is not merely description, it is an entirely deductive process, one of rational explanation. Darwin's is the only rational theory of biological evolution, but its logic is false, so his theory—which deduces the biological structure of the universe from the selectionist hypothesis—is false.

The law of bivalence is a valid law of mathematical language but *not* a mathematical logical law of the universe. The law of causality is a mathematical logical law of the universe but *not* a logical law of mathematical language. So the question arises: What is the law of implication for mathematical language, given that causality is the law of universal implication? Philosophers claim that the law of implication is no more than the law of material implication.

First, we construct the mathematical law of implication of mathematical language (mathematics) by analogy with the law of causality: we define the mathematical law of implication as the pair (A,B) such that A implies B of necessity but B may also imply A. (A,B) is not an ordered pair as for causality in that if A causes B, then B *never* causes A. A material implication of the form "P implies Q" is true so long as it is not the case that P is true and Q is false. Material implication implies that a falsehood implies anything true or false since the following reasoning is correct: "P and not P" $\Rightarrow$ P $\Rightarrow$ "P or Q" (where Q is anything true or false) but "not P" therefore Q. Since "P and not P" is false (law of non-contradiction), a falsehood implies Q, as just proven, where Q is anything true or false. Material implication is no different in its logical structure from the law of mathematical implication.

Axiom 15, the law of non-contradiction, states that a proposition and its negation cannot both be true. If P is true it symbolises reality; the negation of P cannot symbolise reality, so it cannot be true. The meaning of the law is that P and its negation cannot both symbolise reality and so cannot both be true. It is not logical to deny this. The word true is no longer a concept adrift but is anchored in the logic of the universe.

With the assumption of the truth of the law of non-contradiction, the Liar Paradox is resolved. Consider the paradox in the form: "This (very) statement (S) is false". If it is true it is false; so if it is true, it is both true and false, which is impossible (law of non-contradiction), so it's not true. If it's false it's true; so if it's false it's both true and false, which is impossible (contradiction) so it's not false. So it's neither true nor false. Thus there are nonmathematical linguistic statements which are neither true nor false. The law of bivalence, which states that a proposition must be either true or false, is only true for mathematical language, it is not a mathematical law of universal logic. Logicians have developed an unhealthy fear of this paradox, their critical faculties being suspended in its presence. This is not surprising since it drove its inventor potty. Unable to abandon the holy grail of the law of bivalence, they assume its unqualified truth and deduce that the fall guy, the law of non-contradiction (would you believe!) is false. (Some even declare the statement meaningless though it means, unequivocally, what it says.) It is not the meaning, which is in question but its truth value. (Frege misleadingly defines meaning in terms of truth value.) So why is this strange, but seemingly innocent statement unable to truthfully tell us its own truth value. The reason is that the construction of this sentence implies the existence of a formal mathematical system, which is rich enough for the Godel theorem to be applicable. If this were not so the system, that is the proposition, would be consistent and complete so it would tell us the truth about itself. The proposition is not contradictory, so it is incomplete and cannot state its own truth value. The reason is that no consistent (that is, non-contradictory) formal system, which is sufficiently rich in axioms, can apply its theorems to its truth defining concepts without becoming complete and therefore inconsistent. The logical circle cannot be closed without contradiction. This is not just true of semantics but of any logical system. S is a statement about logical truth; but it is also a statement about a statement, which would be all right if that was all it was but it is a statement about the logic of that statement and so falls foul of Godel. S is not contradictory: it is not both true and false, it is neither. Since it constitutes a linguistic system, consisting of a single sentence, being non-contradictory—that is consistent—it must, if sufficiently rich, be incomplete. So it must contain a statement (it only contains one statement) whose truth value it cannot truthfully state. This can only be discovered from outside the system of spoken language, namely the system of mathematical science, which proves that S is neither true nor false.

Consider this self-referential statement: "This statement, Q, is true" It is not as rich as S, which is a statement of negation, so it might escape the Godel noose; that is, it might be not only true but clever enough to tell us it is true. The price of being rich is that you can't tell anyone. It almost certainly isn't false but it might, like S, be neither true nor false. In our opinion the statement is too poor to tell a lie. S may have got rich through lying. If you could arithmetically encode the sentence, using the method of Godel, you would probably find it was not sufficiently rich. It could be that, whatever the truth might be, it is unknowable, because Q is too logically poor to let us know how to prove it, and our logic is insufficient to come to any definite conclusion. If you meet a beggar in the street and he has no voice, it may be he is a millionaire but he can't tell us. Though Q is a statement about its own logic, it may be sufficiently poor to be both consistent and complete. It is satisfying to think of Q as being true because if this most humble of propositions (which does no more than naively assert its own truth) is false, it would seem that the temple of truth has a hollow base.

Here is one more paradoxical self-referential statement. In the literature it is treated as a rare and exotic bird, fascinating but with no recognizable place in our scheme of things. It is by far the most important of all the paradoxes. The statement is: "This statement, R, cannot be proven to be true." This statement, with a slight alteration, was used by Godel to construct his famous theorem. Unlike the other self-referential propositions, R has the gall, not to mention the effrontery and impudence, to lay down a challenge, inviting us to prove it at our peril. Is its confidence justified or is it just another self-deceiving self-referring statement. R does not claim to be true, it only claims it can't be proven. If it is false it cannot be proven true. Is its boast justified? Is it true, false, or neither true nor false? A moment's thought shows that these questions are easily answered. If it is proven true it is also proven false, because it says that it cannot be proven true, so R cannot be proven true without contradiction. But R says it cannot be proven true, so it's true but cannot be proven so.

To put your mind at rest let's apply reductio ad absurdum to the statement. If it is false and proven false then it cannot be proven true. But it is not false, since if it is so it can be proven true by its own admission, which is contradictory. R is known to be true but it cannot be proven by rational thought. It is known to be true solely by an act of faith. Why should we believe this proposition at face value but not the other self-referential propositions? R does not say that it is true or false but that it is undecidable, which it is. It is undecidable because it is consistent (non-contradictory) and just as rich in content as the Liar paradox, so, by Godel's theorem, it is incomplete, that is it contains an undecidable (unprovable) proposition, namely itself. But this is precisely what it tells us, so it is true. It pays a heavy price for telling the truth: while the truth value of the other self-referential propositions can be deduced by rational thought, the truth value of R cannot be so. R is an icy maiden, which attracts us with one hand, inviting we knights of logic to rescue her from the noose of Godel, but repels our rational analysis with the other. The others attract us with their wiles but lie through their teeth. Mathematicians now recognise, because of Godel's theorem, that all mathematics is built on faith. But scientists do not yet recognise that this is true of *all* science. The significance of this astounding paradox is that it forces us to ask whether this is really some uniquely rare bird or whether all scientific birds, whatever their plumage, have this very same character. The entire edifice of knowledge, scientific or otherwise, is built on faith in an unknowable transcendental reality. It is not only the truth of mathematical language which is built on faith. All knowledge is ultimately built on faith. We know it is true that reality is unknowable but it is beyond reason and can only be known by faith. The heart has its reasons, says the poet, reasons which the mind cannot know. The mind has knowledge, which the mind, with its reasoning, cannot know.

Since our ontological logic of the universe is built entirely on the basis of unknowability, it is necessarily the case that quantum physics is also, analogously, built on a foundation of unknowability. All logic, all science, is ultimately founded on concepts which are defined to be unknowable.

The wisest man is he who claims to be most ignorant! For science to evolve, the bounds of knowledge must be rigorously defined. This is not from fear of the unknown, or from a lack of confidence in what science is capable of, but from the need to scientifically define the known. The quark which has seduced physicists with its charm must now be numbered together with the Higg's boson, a drunken concept, which boozes on and on in triumphalist declamation; and of course the virginal vacuum, miraculously pregnant with the universe, as being among the ever increasing legion of mythical concepts (not forgetting travel in reverse time, by increasingly tacky tachyons), whose investigation since the 1930s, has replaced genuine discovery in physical theory.

Consider the Liar Paradox in the form: "This (very) statement (Q) is not true". By the same reasoning, as for the liar paradox, it is proven that the statement is not "T or not T". Thus, there are nonmathematical linguistic propositions, which contradict the so-called law of the excluded middle. There is no such law of the universe. In mathematical language "false" means "not true" since the law of bivalence is true for mathematical language; but in universal logic a statement which is not true may also be not false since (axiom 14) in universal logic there are statements which are neither true nor false. This is also true for mathematical universal logical or structural propositions, as the following examples illustrate. "Reality has a temperature", is a mathematical statement about the thing which creates the universe, so it is a logical statement of mathematical universal science. Since reality is unknowable, one cannot say of it "T or not T". A similar conclusion applies to the statement: "When a hydrogen atom is in a superposed state its electron spends most of its time in the ground state", since properties in the superposed state are unknowable.

Consider, P: "This statement is meaningless". If true, by definition, it symbolises reality. But if true, it is meaningless and so does not symbolise reality. Thus it does and does not, symbolise reality. This result is impossible (non-contradiction); so it is not true. That is, P is meaningful. No system can, truthfully, assert of itself that it is false, or not true, or meaningless. The explanation of this is that a proposition cannot both symbolise and not symbolise reality. This proves that the concept of a defined reality is essential for the resolution of logical paradox. It disproves the claim of some logical ontologists that truth is a trivial concept. If truth is so trivial, then their claim, if true, is trivial, so why bother... their claim is not just trivial, it is absurd. Neither is it true. "Cockroaches ride bicycles" is meaningful but not true. P is meaningful but not true. But what is the meaning? It cannot be that it is meaningless, since then it would be true but it has just been proven that it is not true. P is logically self-referential but not self-contradictory, since it does not state that it is both meaningful and meaningless. So it is consistent but incomplete, which is why, since Godel is applicable, it cannot tell us the truth about itself. P is not true but it may be neither true nor false.

If P is false, it is meaningful because it says it is meaningless. But what can the meaning be? If the meaning is that it is meaningless then it is true; so it is both true and false which is contradictory, so the meaning cannot be that it is meaningless. So, if P is false it has a meaning, but the meaning is unknowable. P cannot be assumed to be true without contradiction, so P is not true. If it is assumed false its meaning exists but is unknowable. But the only meaning it could possibly have, if it has a meaning, is the meaning, which is the set of the semantic relations of its words. But it cannot have that meaning since that meaning is that it is meaningless and it is not meaningless. So P is not false. We conclude that P is neither true nor false. Are there any other statements, which are neither meaningful nor meaningless. Possibly the fine print of many legal documents are deliberately constructed to be of this kind. Politicians who use spin are particularly adept at making such propositions: "The conditions for our entry into the Euromarket..." might be a proposition which is neither meaningful nor meaningless.

All the logical-semantic paradoxes can be resolved by the ontological set of axioms. We begin with the solution of Grelling's paradox. This involves two predicates to find as follows: A predicate is "autological" if it applies to itself. Thus 'polysyllabic' and 'short' are autological since the first is polysyllabic and the second short. A predicate is 'heterological' if it is not autological. Is the predicate 'heterological' heterological? If it is, then it is autological which is contradictory. If it is not then it is both autological and heterological which is also contradictory. Heterological is a concept which defines the logic of the linguistic system, so it can only be applied without contradiction to those members of the system which are not logically defining terms; so it cannot be applied to itself, since this makes the logical system complete and therefore contradictory. Self-reference itself does not produce a contradiction. Whenever the logical circle is closed, a contradiction arises, since the system is complete. This is a consequence of Godel's completeness theorem. You can list items but you cannot list the lists without contradiction. The police cannot investigate themselves without contradiction. A searchlight cannot scan itself. The Liar Paradox is incomplete, not because it is self-referential but because it is *logically* self-referential: if it had just said: "I am a cocoa bean", no problem; but it presumes to define truth within a box, sealing truth within that statement which is its own self. The price it pays for its self-pride, in presuming to truthfully express a truth about its own truth, is that it has rendered itself neither true nor false. But, just as interestingly, it tells us that there is no law of excluded middle, and that there is logic beyond that of mathematical language. For the latter, "not false" means true but this is not true of universal logic, in which it means either true, or, neither true nor false... There must be an unknowable centre, a dark place, at the heart of any consistent logic and faith in the unprovable consistency of that logic. A faith based on reasoning from a set of logical axioms, freely invented from the imaginative resources of mind. This brings science closer to art, since artistic expression claims to bring the mind, as near as it can, to a dark area of unattainable truth which lies beyond the power of expression.

The Berry paradox names a number, a concept of mathematical language, in spoken language. It then uses mathematical language (arithmetic) circularly to count the number of words in the logically naming phrase expressed in words thereby producing, inevitably, a contradiction because of logical circularity. Words → number → words. For example, "Find the smallest number that cannot be named in less than fourteen words." This is a paradox since the sentence itself is an expression naming the number using only 13 words! If you force a dog to chase its own tail, don't be surprised if it barks. Theorems deduced from logic cannot be applied to the logical structure itself without contradiction.

Richard's paradox arises in the following way. A list is made of all the numbers which can be expressed in spoken language, hopefully, at any rate, because doing so creates a whale of a paradox. Construct a number from all these numbers, by drawing a diagonal through them, and altering each number on the diagonal. This number, paradoxically, is on the list, since the list is a list of all numbers that are expressible in speech, yet is not on the list, because it differs from all other numbers on the list, in at least one number, namely the diagonal number. So the number, contradictorily, is both on, and not on, the list. The concept of list is metamathematical, not being a number. It is a logical concept, describing mathematics from outside the system of mathematics. The paradox is resolved, by observing that words define numbers on a list; then this concept of list is used to define in words yet another number. The latter, in mathematical language, does not appear on the list, but since it is also expressed in speech, it does. The contradiction is produced by closing the logical circle so: W → L → W (L = list).

The construction of this number suggests of course, that it has some profound mathematical meaning. It means that you cannot, countably, list all the numbers, which can be expressed in language, since this number is uncountably infinite. Ignoring the contradiction, and adding the diagonalised number to the list, doesn't help, since a new such diagonalized number is waiting in the wings to torment you. It is sometimes wrongly concluded, because of an inability to resolve the paradox, that spoken language cannot express all the numbers that exist. Spoken language cannot express, in a countable list, all the numbers which it can express; but with an advance in set theory, with a new set of axioms, analogous to the creation of nonlinear geometry, it can express numbers not in a countable list.

The hangman's paradox is a veritable pain in the neck. It is not in the mainstream of semantic or conventionally logical paradoxes, because it is neither. A judge, seeking revenge on liberal authority, tells a convict who has been found guilty of murder, that he will be hanged the following week, on any day from Monday to Friday, without any prior warning of the day of the event, so it will come as a surprise. The convict, who has turned his years of incarceration to good account by reading logic and philosophy, triumphantly tells the judge that the hanging cannot take place, arguing so: If the chief warder waits till the last day, Friday, there is no surprise, so no hanging. If he waits till Thursday, the convict will know that, since it cannot happen on Friday it must happen on Thursday, so again, no surprise...and so on till Monday. So no surprise on any day of the week. The judge, a reader of Aristotle, is nonplussed to find he cannot refute this logic, though the convict, logic or no, is not saved by it but is duly hung; on the Tuesday, as it happens. He has to admit that he is surprised to find the noose around his neck.

The convict is making the following proposition: P: "For

any day Z, Monday to Friday - If there is no surprise after day Z, then there is no surprise on day Z." Let us denote this by:

if A, then B

Since A implies B then we must have "not B implies not A". But "not B" is the statement that "there is a surprise on day Z". Thus the convict is hung on day Z since the surprize consists of his being hung. This means that he cannot be surprised after day Z, and thus "not B implies A". We now have the logical contradiction that "not B implies both A and not A". Therefore the original proposition, P, is false, which resolves the paradox. It has been reported that the last words of the convict were, "Who hangs the hangman?"

The resolution of the paradox is that the judge cannot state as fact that the prisoner is guaranteed to be surprised. That statement itself is false. We can enlighten the situation somewhat by considering instead a choice of a card out of five cards. Suppose there are four aces and one joker. The judge tells the prisoner to choose one card at a time until the joker has been drawn. He tells the prisoner that he will be completely surprised when he draws the joker. This claim is false because if the joker is the fifth card drawn, he will not be surprised. When the first card is drawn, the probability of it being a joker is $1/5$. So clearly the prisoner will indeed be surprised if he draws the joker first. The same is true for the second, third and fourth drawings. As long as the probability remains below 1, the prisoner will be surprised (by definition). If the second last drawing reveals an ace thus guaranteeing that the last card is a joker, then the probability is 1 and the prisoner is not surprised when he draws the last card. Notice that the judge is not *completely* wrong. There is $119/120$ probability that the prisoner will draw the joker before the last drawing. This means that 119 out of 120 prisoners given this choice will indeed be surprised. There is a $1/120$ chance that the joker will be the final card drawn.

This probability is not zero and hence the judge cannot claim that the prisoner will be surprised upon the drawing of the joker. The judge would be perfectly correct in saying that the prisoner is *highly likely* to be surprised, but not that he will definitely be surprised.

Now that you accept that the claim of the judge is false, we will outline a sense in which his claim is in fact correct! If the prisoner draws an ace as the second last card he is immediately surprised! He is not surprised by the drawing of a joker, but by the knowledge that he will draw the joker as the next card. In the context of hanging this situation would occur on the second last day. The moment the prisoner realises that he is not to be hung that day, he is surprised to realise that he is to be hung tomorrow! Thus even if the prisoner is indeed hung on the last day he will be surprised by it. The only difference being the day in which the surprise occurs. The judge indeed tells the truth! On the second last day (if he makes it that far) the prisoner will have two opportunities for surprise. If he is hung, it will come as a surprise, but also the moment that he realises that he is *not to be hung*, that too will be a surprise, i.e. he will be surprised by the knowledge of his guaranteed hanging on the following day. So regardless of the day of hanging, the prisoner is surprised when he realises it.

Truth dare not look upon its own face for fear of what it will see. The defining concepts of grammar cannot be applied to themselves without contradiction: What is a verb? A verb is a noun. Contradiction. The paradoxes arise because the truth-defining conditions of the system are applied self-referentially such as to make the system complete and therefore contradictory.

The logical systems of mathematics are birds looking for a place to land. They have no logical ground in truth or reality. Mathematics becomes meaningless when divorced from universal truth. Mathematicians believe absolute mathematical truth does not exist because valid linear and non-linear geometries use contradictory axioms, from which they deduce that the geometry of the world is purely an empirical matter. No. These axioms are absolutely true, all laws symbolise reality. They are true in context, in their respective axiomatic sets. Truth cannot be watered down. *Truth is not relative but absolute.* This is not contradicted by the assertion that truths are true, only in context. This quantum theory proves that different kinds of geometry are true in different physical contexts. Truth and reality are concepts created by the human mind as absolute, on the basis of rationally justified faith. True faith is the faith which believes in truth and defines truth, scientifically, in terms of faith. It is a matter of transcendental belief that there is a reality that lies beyond experience and so beyond consciousness. This ontological system of logic is the first of five. The other four are the linguistic, the relativistic, the quantum, and the biotic systems. The relativistic system is formulated after a linguistic theory has been formulated.

Before the new physics is described, a theory of linguistics must first be proposed because biotic systems are essentially different from abiotic systems in that they contain encoding structures. The reason for this must be found in the evolution and origin of prebiotic systems. What happened at the origin of a prebiotic system to make the existence of encoding inevitable? The microstructures of abiotic systems are sets of invariant *causal* relations between physical interactions (invariance under GCT, that is general coordinate transformations). A prebiotic system marks a radical divergence from this. At the very beginning of its existence, evolution struck out in a radically new direction culminating, deterministically, in the development of symbolic language in animals, with unconscious mind, and the development of conceptual language-speech-with the conscious mind of man. This was the creation of invariant *acausal* relations between physical interactions. All language systems, conscious or unconscious, symbolic, speech, or mathematical, are constructed in this way and are all anticipated by the prebiotic system. This would seem to be immediately contradicted by the Miller experiment of 1953 which constructed amino acids from simple constituents by what would appear to be everyday causal abiotic process. These amino acids are not those of prebiotic and biotic systems, since they have no single chirality (handedness) that is, they are racemic. The amino acids of a prebiotic system are formed, for the first time, by the formation of a set of invariant acausal relations between CPT violating molecular interactions. You can get the feel of the difference between causal and acausal relations by thinking about the structure of games. In constructing a jigsaw puzzle, it makes no logical difference whether you put the first piece down last, or the last piece down first, since the process of construction is entirely reversible and therefore acausal. But in constructing a house, an aeroplane, or a bicycle there is a necessary logical causal order in the process, which cannot be ignored. Mathematics is a language, in which it doesn't always matter, logically, whether the theorems are made into axioms or the axioms deduced as theorems, since the logical process is acausal. In order to understand this linguistic analogy with the living process, it is essential to construct a mathematical theory of linguistics and therefore a new logic. Only part of this theory need be given here, that which defines the concept of meaning.

3

A THEORY OF LINGUISTICS

Although there were several great linguistic scientists before Noam Chomsky, for example Saussure, Whorf, Sapir and Bloom, linguistic science only rose above the level of empiricism with the rationalistic theory of Chomsky a few decades ago. But it could not be considered a mature science since it divorced itself, logically, from mathematics, which is the language of science. Psychology, anxious to ape the success of physics, without understanding that it, too, had a similar conceptual problem, was similarly handicapped by its crazy rejection of the concept of consciousness which was deemed by its reductionist zealots to be unscientific. An understanding of this concept is now considered by some physicists and many biologists to be the primary goal of the entire pursuit of science in all its disciplines. Chomsky, though a mathematician and physicist, did not give a mathematical account of linguistics and did not believe that linguistics could be analysed with mathematical logic. Ironically, Frege, the great founder of modern logic, did attempt a neo-mathematical analysis of sentence structure a few generations earlier but with little success and failed—as all others since—to solve the central problem of the definition of meaning. The whole purpose of language is to convey meaning, but what does this mean?; that is: What is the meaning of meaning?

It should be said, at the outset, that no science has ever succeeded in defining its terms, a prospect ruefully contemplated by Einstein in insisting that no one really knew what a photon is. The baby discipline of linguistics presented its parent disciplines with an embarrassing ultimatum: if it was to live, its concepts had to be defined, which meant that their concepts also had to be defined. Out of the mouths of babes and sucklings. Moralistic science is the only science in which laws are expressed in spoken language. All other sciences are expressed in mathematical language. If linguistic science is to evolve it must be expressed in, and defined in, mathematical language. Yet linguists resist the invasion of mathematics into their territory as if it were an alien force. They do not seem to appreciate that mathematics works through analogy as does linguistics. They are haunted by the antithesis of the precision of mathematics as opposed to the inherent ambiguity of spoken language. Since set theory is now the core of mathematics, it is natural to employ it to define meaning.

We shall see that the structures of atom and molecule are defined in terms of sets of invariant relations (invariant under GCT) and that the origin of life entails an inevitable progression in structural evolution, with the formation of sets of invariant relations between molecular interactions. These sets encode, analogous to language formation, the structure of other molecules, engaged in functional activity. It is, then, essential to understand how language is constructed in terms of set theory and to define the difference between spoken and scientific mathematical language, since it is only by understanding the latter that the origin of life can be discovered by mathematical science. We shall find that we do not have to wait for wanderlusting intergalactic Andromedarians (with or without pointed ears) to impart their superior knowledge, nor, anti-climactically, that life arrived, like a cast-off child, neatly packaged in a meteorite. This, of course, begs the question. The Big Bang origin of the universe likewise begs the question of origin.

These solutions abandon logic. The present theory asks the reader to place his or her faith in the process of deductive logic that has so far been given, quite illogically, a bad name it does not merit.

Wittgenstein had a more profound approach to the question of meaning than Frege who, like Bertrand Russell, held to a false objectivist-subjectivist Aristotelian antithesis which characterises and generates their entire analysis and philosophy of language. They were essentially classical thinkers who could not enter into the subjectivism of quantum thinking. Russell was aware of the inadequacies of their approach. The Fregean dilemma, in attempting to define meaning, is well known. With his philosophy of antithesis he considered words to refer to objects or concepts. He was mistaken: every word refers to a concept. The planet Venus was known by some observers as Hesperus, The Morning Star and by others, in different parts of the world and at different times, as Phosphorus, The Evening Star. Now, said Frege, consider the two sentences, 1. Hesperus is Hesperus and 2. Hesperus is Phosphorus. Two statements of identity, but 1. is trivial, while 2. can be checked by observation of the universe. Their meanings cannot be the same, yet Hesperus and Phosphorus have the same object of reference, namely the planet Venus. So meaning cannot consist purely of reference but must have, in addition, what Frege called "sense", that is, the "senses" of Hesperus and Phosphorus must be different, though their reference is the same and their meanings are different because their "senses" are different. The argument appears convincing but proves, on examination, to be unfruitful and contradictory. It is often a good idea to turn logic on its head because sometimes we are looking through the wrong end of the logical telescope.

We begin by abolishing the object-concept distinction of Frege in order to obtain the widest possible range of application of the concept of concept. It is assumed that the meaning of a word is a concept. The next logical step is, then, to define, in terms of set theory, what is meant by the concept of concept. There are as many definitions of concept as there are philosophies of logic and language. So, for the reasons stated, we propose the first mathematical definition of concept.

A concept is a set of connotations; each connotation is an element of the set, which identifies the set.

Connotation is an undefined concept. The symbolic relation is defined. A symbolises B if A refers to B. B, the referent of A, is defined as being the meaning of A. Every word is a symbol. The meaning of a word is the concept to which it refers. Finally, we have: the meaning of a word is the concept to which it refers; each connotation of the meaning identifies the meaning. Now let's see if this resolves the Fregean dilemma.

Frege assumes that "The Morning Star" has a meaning. It is composed of words and words have meanings, so it would seem self-evident that the phrase has a meaning and crazy to suggest otherwise. The evolution of logic has taught us that nothing is self-evident (not even self-evidence). Let's learn a lesson from physics: We thought it self-evident that motionless bodies have no energy but $e = mc^2$ taught us otherwise. It is linguistic logic which determines whether a phrase has meaning, not our unconscious intuition. What we should be asking is not What is the meaning of "The Morning Star"? but, reversing the accustomed point of view, asking What is the meaning of Venus? This is a word, and therefore a concept, and all concepts have a meaning. Contrary to Frege, Venus refers to a concept, not an object which is a planet. Since we identify Hesperus and Phosphorus with Venus—we say "Hesperus *is* Venus", "Phosphorus *is* Venus"—the meaning of Venus, from the proposed definition of meaning, is the set of connotations {Hesperus, Phosphorus, ...}. The meaning of Venus is its reference, which is this set; so we do not have the Fregean dilemma of additionally introducing the half-baked notion of "sense" which introduces contradictions.

Sentence 1: "Hesperus is Hesperus", though trivial is true, being a statement of the logical law of identity of mathematical language.

Sentence 2: "Hesperus is Phosphorus" is false since Hesperus, a connotation, is stated to be identical to another connotation of the same meaning-set.

But a set cannot have identical elements; that is, every connotation is different from every other. 1. merely states that a connotation is self-identical. 2. provides substantive (non-trivial) information about Venus but does so illogically. Hesperus and Phosphorus are meaningless in the literal scientific definitional sense of not being meanings but connotations, which are elements of meanings but not, themselves, meanings. A connotation of a meaning cannot have a meaning, by definition. The meaning has connotations, but not the reverse. An element of a set cannot have a set but a set can have elements. It is the set which is the meaning, not the elements of the set, that is, not the connotations of the set. We have been looking through the wrong end of the logical telescope. One must not confuse the law of identity, a logical law of mathematical language, with the logical law of identification, a logical law of the universe. Wittgenstein, failing to appreciate the difference, used to comment on the sterility of the law of identity. *Hesperus is identical to Hesperus. Hesperus and Phosphorus identify (are not identical to) Venus.*

How does this theory relate to what we do when we look up a dictionary to find the meaning of a word? A dictionary tells you that it gives you the enumerated meanings of a word. The word "meaning" when used in this way, is a concept of spoken language but not of scientific linguistic language. The concept of energy has different meanings in spoken and scientific language. These so-called lexical mean-ings, in scientific language, are connotations, not meanings. The meaning of a word is the set of all these connotations. Some words do have different meanings, each with its own set of connotations. A word may begin as a one-element set but all words are able to evolve into many-element sets. Wittgenstein correctly says that meaning is determined by use: it is the acquisition or loss of connotations, which deter-mines the meaning of a word. The meaning of a word evolves. Some words have some preponderantly important connotations, such that a knowledge of them implies a knowledge of the set. It is only a knowledge of the set *as a whole* which justifies the claim that the concept is known and understood. It is possible to know many connotations of a word and still not know the set as a whole and there-fore not know its meaning, and conversely. The meaning of the word "Venus", in our theory, is the set of connotations: 1. Roman goddess of love, 2. the planet second in order of distance from the sun, 3. a beautiful woman. The connota-tions, Hesperus and Phosphorus, are archaic. The meaning is not just the second connotation as it is for Frege. Venus has a meaning but none of these phrases, in mathematical linguistic science, is a meaning. These phrases are connota-tional elements of a meaning but neither is a meaning.

The meaning of a word of spoken language, such as Venus, has no definition, that is, no defining connotation, though some connotations are more important than others in the construction and knowledge of the set. In scientific language, by contrast, a scientific concept must have a def-inition. It cannot be assumed and one would not want to, that definition is an undefined term: it is necessary to define it when it is used in scientific language. A definition is defined as a special kind of connotation, one which causes all the other connotations of the concept. The word "Venus", in spoken language, has no definition, yet the word "word", which is also a word does have a definition. Doesn't this smack of contradictory favouritism? No. By

Godel's theorem, a theorem cannot be applied to the logical concepts from which the theorem is deduced, without contradiction. So the theorem that a word of spoken language has no definition cannot be applied to the scientific linguistic logical concept of word without contradiction. It is contradictory to bite the hand that feeds you. Similarly, the concept of definition in spoken language has, ironically, no definition though it has, and indeed must have, in scientific language. Note that, in scientific language, it is not the concept of connotation which is defined - the concept of definition is defined in terms of the concept of connotation. A definition, in linguistic science, is a special kind of connotation which implies all the others but not inversely. Let's apply the definition of word, to word itself, and see whether it generates its connotations, as it should do, if the definition of definition is correct. The meaning of word is defined as a concept which is its set of identifying connotations. This definition implies the following two connotations of the meaning:

The meaning of a word of spoken language is a concept which is a set of identifying connotations, none of which defines the word.

The meaning of a word of scientific language is a set of identifying connotations, one of which defines the concept, that is, implies its connotations.

This has been expressed at some length since it is important to avoid loose terminology which, ironically, is perhaps a greater temptation in linguistics than in any other science.

The linguistic theory allows us to see the true nature of Kantian analytic a priori propositions. These are supposed to be logical propositions which are true of necessity and say nothing new about the universe. Let us see if this is the case. An example is: "A bachelor is an unmarried man. John is a bachelor. Therefore John is an unmarried man." The meaning of the word bachelor is the set of connotations to which it refers. This set is, briefly, [an unmarried man; a young knight in service; a person who holds a university degree; a young male fur seal]. So it may be that John is married and John is a bachelor, having completed an undergraduate course. Reasoning from meaning is not trivial, since it requires the selection of the correct connotation and this requires knowledge of the world. This knowledge is what the conventional claim about the analytic a priori denies. Here is another similar example. "This animal is a vixen. Therefore it is a female fox." The meaning of the word vixen is the set of connotations [a female fox; a quarrelsome, shrewish or malicious woman.]. Let us suppose that Mab Prendergast is shrewish. Since she is a woman let us suppose that she is a human animal. So, for Mab, we can make this proposition, "This animal is a vixen. Therefore it is shrewish" but not that it is a female fox. We have to know something about the world, namely about Mab and foxes before we can make this judgment.

Here is a more subtle example, involving propositional attitudes. Francis knows of Dr Jekyll as a fine man and eminent doctor. He hopes that Dr Jekyll will accept him as one of his patients. But Dr Jekyll is Mr. Hyde. Francis knows of Mr. Hyde as a dangerous incompetent. He has expressed his abhorrence of him. If we apply the law of identity to the true proposition, that Francis wants Dr Jekyll to become his doctor, we obtain the falsehood that Francis wants Mr. Hyde to become his doctor. Does this mean the law of identity is false? No. Does this mean that Dr Jekyll is not Mr. Hyde? No. Then why is there a contradiction? It arises because the law, which is relevant, is not the law of identity, a logical law of mathematical language, but the law of identification, a logical law of the universe. The correct reasoning is as follows. Dr. Jekyll is a name. A name is a word and therefore a concept. The concept, Dr. Jekyll, is the set of connotations [Dr. Jekyll, the kindly and skilful doctor; Mr. Hyde, the cruel and disturbed incompetent]. Francis does not know the concept but only the first connotation. This connotation identifies—is not identical to—the concept, Dr. Jekyll. But Francis does not identify Mr. Hyde with the concept, so the falsehood does not follow from the truth that Francis wants Dr. Jekyll to become his doctor. The reason for the contradiction is a failure to realise that there exists a logic of the universe and that the law of identification is one of these laws. As a matter of interest, suppose Dr. Jekyll were thought to have died and Mr. Hyde, still a rapscallion, really became a good doctor (which wouldn't be difficult since he already was one!) which would be the concept, Dr. Jekyll or Mr. Hyde? Mr. Hyde's patients would think that Mr. Hyde was the concept. If they got to know about Dr Jekyll's full history they would still think of Mr. Hyde as the concept and Dr Jekyll as a connotation of the concept. The use of the word would determine its hierarchical status.

Here is a famous contradiction, invented by Quine, which has never been resolved because of a failure to appreciate the difference between the law of identity and the law of identification.

It is necessarily true that $9 = 9$ (by the law of identity).
$9 =$ the number of planets.
Therefore, it is necessarily true that $9 =$ the number of planets.

The conclusion would appear to follow from the identity law, but it is false, since it is only contingently true that $9 =$ the number of planets. It might well have been otherwise. So what has gone wrong? In the first mathematical equality the relation of identity obeys the law of necessity. In the second mathematical equality the relation of identification obeys the law of contingency. The number of planets is not identical to the number 9, it is identified by the number 9. (Speech is logically misleading). If it were identical it would be the expression of a law of the universe and so true of necessity. The statement is a fact, contingently true but not a law, true of necessity. A rose by any other name would smell as sweet but the relation of a name to the rose is one of identification not of identity. This relation clearly obeys a law of contingency, not of necessity, because a rose doesn't have to be called a rose. The analogy is difficult to appreciate because we do not say that the name of a rose is equal to a rose, though the naming relation also obeys the law of identification. The real things of the universe are identified by their properties. A system of planets has the property of number. This property is identified by the number 9. The relation of identification does not always obey the law of contingency. Particles are identified by their invariant mass and charge. This relation of identification obeys the law of necessity.

The scientific community has not yet succeeded in defining its concepts. To do so, we must create a new species at a higher level of scientific consciousness. Aristotle, amazingly, even more than two thousand years ago, understood the importance of defining. He said that to define is godlike: to define is divine. Man originated, as Homo habilis, with knowledge of law, that is he knew necessary truths. Animals before this knew only contingent truths, that is, truths which could have been otherwise. He needed to know laws in order to form the concepts of spoken language. He only knew unconsciously the mathematical laws which construct spoken language and so could not define these laws. The meaning of the words of spoken language cannot be defined.

Mathematical language was only discovered 10,000 years ago, so that, until our theory, the concepts of universal science have been undefined. The power of conceptual thinking lies in its ability to organise vast areas of experience. Mathematical concepts, which inherently incorporate organisation in their definition, by raising the organisational capacity of human thinking to a higher level of consciousness, have caused the creation of civilisation. But man's dream to have dominion over the universe will only be achieved when he defines the concepts of science. It is not enough to eat from the tree of morality we must now eat from the tree of life. To do so we must define life and become "as God". This will produce a discontinuity in the organisation of knowledge far exceeding anything which preceded it. This is nothing less than a unification of the sciences, which multiply and diversify, like the branches of a tree, within the consciousness of a single experience, at a higher level of consciousness than any form of cognitive consciousness, including the scientific consciousness which it unifies.

Our theory resolves the Sorites paradox. Like most paradoxes, it looks so easy to resolve until you try it. This one is especially annoying. After countless irritating failures you are forced to admit there is a gap in our knowledge which only a new theory can rectify. To ignore a paradox is to ignore a signpost on the road which leads to truth. The paradox arises if the following question is asked. Suppposing one is of the opinion that a certain man, a Mr. Sawyer, is not bald. Ask the question: will he still be "not bald" if a hair is removed from his head. Surely it cannot, logically, make any significant difference if only a single hair is removed, so the answer must be yes. By the same logic, the state of baldness or not baldness cannot be affected by the removal of another single hair, so, if another hair is removed, he is still not bald and so on for another and another. So, by this seemingly irrefutable logic, when all his hair is removed he is not bald. The paradox arises from the failure to understand that, while the meaning of a scientific linguistic concept, such as meaning, can be defined, the meaning of a word of spoken language cannot. So the meaning of the word "bald" cannot be defined. It cannot, then, be defined in spoken language mathematically(!) by some such premise as "When 999 hairs have been removed he is not bald, but when 1000 hairs have been removed he is bald." There is no mathematical definition of baldness or, indeed, any other definition. The mathematical criterion implies that the proposition, Mr. Sawyer is bald, is either true or false, whereas, for quite a range of hair removal, it is neither true nor false. The judgment as to whether a man is bald is entirely a matter of subjective perception. It is objectively true that bald has a meaning but the judgment of baldness is subjective. While one society may think of him as bald, another society may think of him as hairy. While some members of the same society (hippies) may think of him as very bald, others may think of him as slightly bald or not bald. The meaning of the meaning of a word is defined, but the meaning of a word, in spoken language is undefined. Even if the word is bald, no amount of hair-splitting will make it otherwise. The word "subjective", as used here, has a purely scientific definition: the meaning of a proposition is subjective if it is unrelated to reality. "Chocolate tastes good" is true for some and false for others, so it is not unambiguously stated to be true or false; that is, it is neither true nor false. It cannot be said to symbolise reality or to not symbolise reality. If it could, it would be, by definition, either true or false. It is not an objective but a subjective statement. A statement which is not subjective is objective, by definition. This is contrary to the way these terms are used in spoken language. It is usual to say that feelings are subjective, while sensory experience, which is not illusory, is objective. Our theory establishes that feelings are no less objective than sensory experience. The proposition, "Mr. Sawyer has a pain in his right arm" is objectively true (and not neither true nor false) and his feeling of pain is no less real than his arm.

Special relativity, wrongly interpreted, gave birth to the idea that everything is relative, that there is no such thing as absolute truth, as everything is subjective. The property of non-invariant length symbolises reality, as do all properties, and so is objective. A proposition about the non-invariant length of an object is either true or false. Truth is absolute.

The original Sorites paradox does not attempt to define the undefinable but asks a different question: how we can know the meaning of a word, which is a name, in a particularly ambiguous case. Suppose a famous ship has several repairs in the course of its history of battle at sea. What does the name of the ship refer to? Does it refer to the ship, as originally constructed? Suppose all the original worn timbers, long since removed, are brought together and made into a monument. Is this the original ship, with more right to its name than the construction in which nearly all the original timbers have been replaced, during several episodes of repair?. The name of the ship is a word, so its meaning is a set of connotations. One such connotation could be: "The ship which, after its final major repair, led the Greek navy to victory, under the command of Aghiopopopolis, against the Turks at the battle of X". But if the words "after its final major repair" do not appear in the connotation, then the structure of the ship is irrelevant to the meaning of its name. As for the monument, original though the timbers are, the name of the monument is the name of a ship's monument, not the name of a ship. The final, or preceding, renovated versions of the ship deserve the name of the ship because the ship is an evolving construction used for the purpose of sailing the high seas while, paradoxically, the assembly of original timbers is not. The physical elements of construction of the ship have no necessary relation to the purely logical elements of the meaning of its name. The name of a thing is not the thing itself nor are the connotational elements which construct that name. These elements, which are psychological, are designed to convey the evolution or history of the ship, not to eliminate it by a return to a pristine original material construction.

We have seen that the mathematics of language is set theory. It is a most striking property of living things, at the molecular level, that one kind of molecule programmes the creation of another kind of molecule - a biological computer but no hands and no power plugs. A theory that does not explain this cannot be true. Biosystems behave analogously to information-carrying language systems. This implies that there should be an emphasis on set theory, in a theory of the origin of life. The simplest premise is that while, prior to prebiotic systems, all microstructures were constructed of sets of invariant causal relations, prebiotic systems originated with the birth of a new kind of structure - a set of invariant acausal relations between molecular interactions, which encoded the structure of a different kind of molecule, functionally related by feed-back to this new structure. If the relation really is one of feedback, then information is carried both to and from the encoding molecule, which contradicts currently accepted theory of almost exclusively one-way transmission of information from nucleic acid to protein. The emphasis throughout the theory must be on the concept of evolution. The introduction of different levels of organisation implies that, throughout the course of evolution, different hierarchical levels of emergent structure evolved, based analogously on the evolution of lower levels and introducing, at each level, novel properties, governed by previously nonexisting laws. There are laws which govern the process of change at any level which themselves change, by a process of evolution, to produce the analogous laws of change at successively higher levels of hierarchy. Other writers have expressed this notion but its immensely fruitful possibilities have never been adequately realised.

4

THE LOGICAL
LAWS OF RELATIVITY

The Einstein general theory of relativity (GTR) does not unify quantum and relativity theories for three main reasons:

1. It is not a theory of microscopic interaction.
2. The law of general relativity is not correctly formulated.
3. It is based on the principle of equivalence, which is false.

Covariance is a necessary, but not sufficient, condition for a statement to be a law; there are numerous statements, which are covariant but are not laws. In any real sense Einstein abandoned the theory as one which determined law and it became recognised as a theory of gravity.

This abandonment is apparent from his erroneous interpretation of the clock paradox (the twin paradox), now wrongly accepted as being non-paradoxical. This paradox is as cataclysmic for the GTR as the Schrodinger cat paradox is for orthodox quantum theory. If the travelling twin really did return younger than the stay-at- home twin, an absolute change in the world would have been caused, by a purely metrical change, which contradicts relativity. If you leave money in your will to your mother and want her to enjoy it to a ripe old age, send her off on a very long trip at a very fast speed (almost c) and she will return younger than you, who are on your deathbed. Who said the Darwinists had all the just so stories. Max Born said we just have to learn to accept such things. Really? If you woke up one morning and found your wife had three heads, would you just accept it or would you be logically inclined to ask yourself where you'd been the night before. Of course the twins have different physical experiences - the metric has changed. So what! Why not prepare for a bumpy ride, instead of abandoning the law at the first hurdle. Einstein said, "If we can ignore the accelerations..." How can the "ignorable" accelerations also be the cause of the physical change, without contradiction? As with Darwin's theory, physicists talk at, not to, each other. Physicists have been told this umpteen times but you might as well talk to the wall. The Einstein theory is schizophrenic. The twins, as GTR adherents rightly insist, must behave like the clocks. But how do the clocks behave? This cannot be deduced from the equivalence principle, because this is false. We resolve the paradox by redefining the law of general relativity as follows: a universal structural law is covariant and metric determinant.

The behaviour of the travelling clock is determined by the processes of the travelling twin. The laws of the biological processes of the travelling twin are unknown but it is they that determine the metric, that is, the way that the clock behaves and *not the reverse*. This is sufficient to resolve the paradox. It could be that in all probability the laws obeyed by the travelling twin are unchanged by the act of travelling in which case the returning clock is determined by this fact to have the same reading as the stationary clock. This contradicts the generally accepted view that the travelling clock must return with a different time to the stationary clock. All that is necessary to resolve a paradox is to indicate a logical flaw in its construction. This has been done, which resolves the paradox.

Einstein correctly postulates a second law of universal logic: the proper rate of a clock and the proper length of a rod are non-invariant under GCT. This is supported, experimentally, by the Mossbauer effect. A peculiarity of this law is that it is a statement of invariance about noninvariance. It is invariantly the case that noninvariance exists, it seems to stand logic on its head. Another quantum general relativistic law of logic is obtained, by analogy with a logical law of Einstein's special theory. Einstein's special theory relates the logical laws of special relativity, to Maxwell's structural law of the constancy of the velocity of light, to produce another logical law of the special theory. This says that the time interval between events, connectible by particle transmission, is invariant under linear transformations (Euclidean); the time interval between events, not connectible by particle transmission, is non-invariant under linear transformations.

Since the present theory is causally deterministic, causality, as defined in axiom 17 of the ontological set, is introduced. The causal pairing need not be time-ordered, as well as logically ordered, but it may be. In the non-living world, in the case of interactions causing interactions by particle transmission, we assume, analogously, an invariant under GCT time-ordered relation between the causally related interactions; interactions which are not causally related by particle transmission, have a non-invariant, under GCT, time ordered relation. As we shall see, it is the violation of this logical law, in living systems, because of a new kind of interaction, which occurs only in prebiotic and living systems, which gives the secret of the origin of life. It is the violation of this law, which makes free will possible. Contrary to what J. B. Watson, Patricia Churchland, and other reductionists say, biotic systems have a logic separate from that of abiotic systems. It will be seen, from this new quantum logic for nonliving systems, that the correlations produced with entanglement, as described in the EPR paradox, must be assumed to be causal correlations. Their causal time ordering is nonvariant under GCT. This does not obey the time-ordering law just posited, so nonlocality cannot, then, be produced by particle transmission, but must be produced by some other means. How is a particle to be defined to produce such a causal relation, one not communicated by particle transmission, and yet, nevertheless, causally communicated? This question will be answered later. Before this is done, a unified quantum-relativistic thermodynamic theory is formed, by deducing some quantum *structural* laws of the universe, from the logical laws just formulated. These logical laws are listed.

The Logical Laws of General Relativity

The law of general relativity says that a universal structural law is covariant under GCT and metric determinant. The proper rate of a clock and the proper length of a rod are non-invariant under GCT.

There is a logical law of causality: the law of causal implication is an ordered pair (A, B); A implies B of necessity, but B does not imply A. A is the cause of B.

Interactions, which are causally related by particle transmission, have an invariant, under GCT, time-order relation; interactions, which are not causally related, by particle transmission, have a non-invariant, under GCT, time-order relation.

5

A QUANTUM-RELATIVISTIC
THEORY OF THERMODYNAMICS

The Microscopic Structural Laws of Interaction

An asymmetric interaction is defined as one which violates one or more symmetry transformations; a symmetric interaction is one which does not violate any symmetry transformation. Since causality is an asymmetric relation (of implication) only asymmetric interactions are assumed to cause. By symmetry, they cause both kinds of interaction, asymmetric and symmetric. We deduce this first structural law: asymmetric interactions cause asymmetric and symmetric interactions; symmetric interactions do not cause any kind of interaction. The revised law of general relativity requires that this law be metric determinant and not only covariant. Since causality, effected by particle transmission, is always logically associated with invariance, it is the causing asymmetric interactions, which must be taken to be invariant, under GCT. So, we have a second structural law, one which is not only covariant, but which determines the microscopic metric: asymmetric interactions are invariant under GCT and determine the microscopic metric; symmetric interactions are non-invariant under GCT and not metric determinant.

The laws of interaction are related to the classical laws of thermodynamics, which they must explain micromechanically and formulate quantum-relativistically. The second law of thermodynamics stands as a monumentally imposing edifice in the mainstream of classical physics-sublime but enigmatic. One is tempted to say sublime yet ridiculous, since it defies our classical sense of logic. The source of the enigma is that classical laws are symmetry conserved, so cannot in principle explain the temporal asymmetry of the second law. In addition, the meaning of entropy is going through a Kuhnian sea change. Instead of Boltzmann's measure of disorder or chaos, we now tend to think of entropy as being a measure of organisation in time. This is because we are now more interested in constructing than in analysing (holism versus reductionism). It must not be thought, however, that this is just a change of fashion, as Kuhn would have us believe, Truth really does exist. We shall define the entropy of a system (micro or macro) as the measure of its organisation in time, which is the probabilistic measure of the energy availability of its energy states. To the professor's wife, his room is in a mess, a state of disorder with nothing in its place, but to the professor his room is highly organised, because everything is readily available.

Work and heat are strongly correlated but they are no less puzzling than entropy. Since work is spatially organised energy, and heat is unorganised energy, how can work have nothing to do with entropy if both are a measure of organisation. The classical definition of entropy has an unexplained, and illogical, bias in favour of heat. What does this mean? Clearly, a huge revolution in thermodynamics is required. We replace the symmetry-conservation of classical theory with binary asymmetry-symmetry and binary conservation-non-conservation. We must arrive at a definition of work and heat in terms of organisation. They are both solely macroscopic concepts, whereas entropy is both a microscopic and a macroscopic concept. Work is the measure of the macroscopic transfer of spatially organised—that is spatially directed—energy, caused by asymmetric inter-actions; heat is the measure of the macroscopic transfer of spatially unorganised—that is spatially undirected—energy across a temperature boundary caused by symmetric inter-actions. Symmetric interactions do not cause microscopic interactions but do cause macroscopic change. Physicists have been toying with the idea of real non-conservation of energy, which we sweep under the carpet of the misunder-stood Heisenberg uncertainty principle. Since asymmetric interactions are symmetry non-conserved, we assume they are also energy non-conserved. Symmetry conserving inter-actions are assumed to be energy conserved. This means that the so-called energy conserved asymmetric interactions of radioactivity are weakly non-conserved. This leads, of necessity, to the additional postulate that some of these interactions (depending on context) are momentum non-conserved also. Let's apply this to an isolated macrosystem.

Thermodynamics of an Isolated Macrosystem

Since each (microscopic) asymmetric interaction makes a scalar contribution of de, the measure of the non-conserva-tion of the total energy of the interaction, to the total ener-gy, E, of the macrosystem, it follows that entropy is defined, mathematically, by

$$dS = dE/\theta \qquad (1)$$

(θ is the temperature of the macrosystem; dE is the differ-ential change in the total energy of the macrosystem, which is the scalar sum of the microscopic changes, de.). This is consistent with regarding all changes of energy as con-tributing to changes in entropy. Since macroscopic temporal asymmetry cannot be logically explained, in terms of micro-scopic temporal symmetry, it is assumed that T is violated for any interaction which contributes, asymmetrically, to macroscopic entropy change. It is assumed that for isolated systems, CPT is not violated. Since T is violated, CP is violated so that that C or P is violated. You cannot logically explain why a coin always turns up heads if you posit that the other side is a tail. T violating interactions cause the macrosystem, in the non-equilibrium state, to be both entropy and energy non-conserved. These interactions contribute an unbalanced energy and entropy change to the system. Asymmetric interactions, which do not violate T, do not conserve energy and so do not conserve entropy either, because of the latter's definition, but because they do not violate T, they contribute only balanced (zero net) entropy change to the macrosystem in the non-equilibrium and equilibrium state. (An interaction and the time-reversed interaction cause equal and opposite changes of entropy which is not the case when T is violated). The energy change for these interactions is balanced for the non-equilibrium state, (as well as the equilibrium state), so the total energy, E, of an isolated macrosystem, in the nonequlibrium state, is non-conserved. Since entropy increases unilaterally, total energy clearly also increases unilaterally due to the definition of entropy. The definition of entropy is consistent with the interactions which cause it. The net entropy-energy change of the system is caused by T violation. Total energy is conserved, in the equilibrium state, because this state is entropy conserved. This does not mean that there are no T violating interactions in the equilibrium state: it means that, in a limiting sense, there is a balance between the entropy change for a T violating interaction and the time reversed interaction. The T violation is then minimal. We shall see that T violation occurs in molecules and they are, of course, present in the equilibrium state also. Perfect equilibrium is an unreal mathematically idealised state, not a physically real state. In the non-equilibrium state there is a positive imbalance in entropy production; in the equilibrium state there is an imbalance which tends to zero. Interactions which violate both C and P do not cause entropy imbalance because they do not violate T. In the equilibrium state, T violating interactions cause balanced entropy and energy change, so entropy and energy are conserved. This is the third structural law. This binary law of non-conserved-conserved energy for interactions and isolated systems must be metric determinant and so it must produce a structural law which specifies the asymmetric interactions of the system since it is they which are metric determinant. It does this because the entropy law, the second law of thermodynamics, is expressed so: the entropy of an isolated macrosystem in the non-equilibrium state always increases; the entropy of the equilibrium state is conserved, being a maximum in that state. Since asymmetric interactions cause both kinds of interaction, asymmetric and symmetric, both kinds of interaction are present in both equilibrium and non-equilibrium states. Symmetric interactions, being energy conserved, make no entropy contribution in either state. Asymmetric interactions, which do not violate T, make a balanced entropy contribution in either state. Those which violate T do not make a balanced (energy and) entropy contribution in the non-equilibrium state: in this state, their entropy contribution is always biased in a specific time direction, which is defined as the direction of increasing time (the "arrow of time"); in the equilibrium state their entropy and energy contribution is balanced, the entropy being a maximum. The microscopic structural law, which explains the second law is: the unbalanced entropy contribution of T violating interactions causes the unilateral increase of entropy of an isolated macrosystem; their balanced entropy contribution causes the equilibrium state of maximum entropy.

This fourth structural law is necessary to resolve the question of reduction of the wavefunction. It completes the work, begun by Boltzmann, more than a century ago. Since T violation causes macroscopic entropy change, the change of organisation of energy in time, it is inevitable, analogously, to assume that C and P violation cause the performance of work, the macroscopic change of organisation of energy in space. Violation of C must cause electromagnetic work but what does P violation cause? To answer this question and to define the nature of the particle as proposed earlier, we need a new set of logical quantum postulates. Existing quantum logic cannot do this. Symmetric interactions do not cause interactions but they cause the creation of heat, defined as the macroscopic transfer of spatially unorganised (chaotic) energy, that is, energy which is non-directed in space, caused by symmetric interactions. Work is defined as the macroscopic transfer of spatially organised (spatially directed) energy, caused by asymmetric interactions. The latter also cause entropy increase if they violate T. These are the first definitions of work and heat. In the equilibrium state, analogous to the balance of entropy (-energy), there is a balance of heat and work transfer, not present in the non-equilibrium state. Symmetric interactions in the non-equilibrium state though they conserve energy, cause an imbalanced flow of heat, that is, there is heat dissipation in the system. Analogously, asymmetric interactions which violate C and P but not T, by symmetry, though they conserve entropy, cause net unbalanced internal work. The state of equilibrium is not a state of maximum disorder but the opposite: a state of maximum organisation. Moreover, the symmetric interactions, which do cause disordered macroscopic motion of energy in the form of heat in this state, cause an ordered balance of this disordered energy! Order out of chaos. This may appear paradoxical: how can disorder be a source of order? The paradox is resolved by observing that symmetric interactions are caused by asymmetric ones which cause macroscopic order. The source of macroscopic disorder lies in macroscopic order. When the latter is balanced the former is balanced. The order out of chaos, deduced here, has nothing to do with the origin of life, which does not arise from chaos.

All quantum theories have failed, thus far, to unify gravity and quantum theory in a satisfactory way. This unification follows easily if we interpret P violating interactions, analogous to C violating interactions causing electro-magnetic work, as causing gravitational work. It follows that there are only two forces in the universe: electromagnetic and gravitational, since there are only three kinds of symmetry violation and T violation causes entropy change. See Table 1. This is only a partial unification of force. To complete it, we must later find how force operates at the micro level to produce the macromechanical laws of motion. Entropy is defined as the measure of organisation of a macro system, which is the probabilistic availability of its energy states. It is a measure of relatedness rather than chaos. Logically, organisation at the macro-level must come from organisation at the micro-level. But how is the organisation of the particle which produces this organisation to be defined? What does it mean to say a particle is an organisation? Clearly, the concept of organisation must be defined. Before doing this it is necessary to relate the quantum theory of thermodynamics to classical thermodynamics, to which the former must reduce in the case of a reversible process. By so doing we shall discover the real meaning of classical theory.

Table 1

MICROSCOPIC INTERACTIONS	CONSERVATION	MACROSCOPIC CAUSATION
1. symmetric	energy and entropy conserved	cause formation of heat only
2. C and P; not T	energy and entropy non-conserved	cause electromagnetic and gravitational work; not entropy (entropy balance)
3. C or P; and T	energy and entropy non-conserved	cause electromagnetic or gravitational work; and entropy

The Meaning of Classical thermodynamics

We deduce from this thermodynamic theory: the quantum-general relativistic non-conserved energy equation for a closed system in a reversible or irreversible process, is:

$$dE = dQ + dW + de \tag{2}$$

dE is the differential change in the non-conserved total energy of the system.
de is the differential change in the non-conserved total energy of the asymmetric interactions.
dQ is the differential transfer of heat.
By analogy with classical theory entropy is defined by $dS = dE/\theta$ (θ is the absolute temperature of the system.)

All the work of the system is caused by the non-conserved energy de. Symmetric interactions do not cause work, only heat transfer. The maximum amount of work an interaction can cause is equal to its non-conserved energy, de. In any process, reversible as well as irreversible, (2) is the process equation, energy being non-conserved for reversible as well as irreversible process. It is solely non-conserved energy which drives nature, which makes things happen. Conserved energy is always chaotic energy, energy which is symmetrical with no particular directionality. Cause cannot be defined in a physics in which energy is conserved. Bertrand Russell remarked that the concept of causality never appears in any physical law. Our theory explains why. In the limiting case of a reversible process work is produced most efficiently. The theory must explain this and, microscopically, why entropy increase is always less for a reversible than for an irreversible process. Consider the isothermal expansion of a Carnot engine. The quantum equation must reduce to the classical for entropy increase:

$$dS = dQ/\theta = dE/\theta$$

therefore

$$dQ = de \tag{3}$$

$$dE = dQ + dW + de \tag{2}$$

$$dW + de = 0 \tag{4}$$

So, all the non-conserved energy causes useful work. But in an irreversible process $dS > dQ/\theta$, since $dE = dQ + de - dW$, where $(de - dW)$ is positive, because the process is less efficient; there is an additional entropy $dS = de - dW/\theta$ being produced. In the reversible process, the non-conserved energy is expending itself entirely on spatial organisation work. Whereas in the irreversible process, it is also expending itself in increasing temporal organisation, entropy, at the expense of work. You don't get nowt for nowt. There is a price to be paid for maximum efficiency. The process is infinitely slow. The process cannot be strictly reversible since without asymmetry there is no causation and no work production.

In an irreversible process there are T violating interactions which increase the entropy of the system more than in a reversible one, at the expense of work production. Classically, in the reversible case

$$dU = dQ - dW = 0 \tag{5}$$

U is internal energy

The corresponding quantum equation for the reversible case is:

$$dE = dQ - dW + de = dQ = dW = de \tag{6}$$

The classical description of this process is that the system absorbs heat, which causes work to be done. The correct description, that of quantum theory, is that the absorption of heat causes the equilibrium state to be disturbed: T violating interactions no longer have an entropy or work balance; it is this which causes the entropy of the system to change and the system to do work. Heat never causes work to be done. If heat is added reversibly to a closed system doing no work, the T violating interactions produce an entropy imbalance, which increases the entropy of the system, but no work imbalance. Heat does not cause work to be done, the asymmetric interactions do, but the work is balanced. If a system in a Carnot cycle absorbs heat Q1 on the first isothermal and rejects heat Q2, on the second isothermal, it returns to its initial state unchanged; but its total energy, E, has increased by Q1-Q2, since E is not a state function. For an isolated system, which undergoes an irreversible process,

$$dE = dQ + dW + de = 0 + 0 + de = de \tag{7}$$

$$dS = dE/\theta = de/\theta \tag{8}$$

de is the imbalance in the non-conserved total energy, E, of the system, produced by T violation. Since $dS > 0$, the universe is composed of self-organising systems. In the equilibrium state, $de = 0$ and $dS = 0$.

For an adiabatic process in which work is done, $dE = dQ + dW + de = 0 + dW + de$, therefore $dE = dW + de$; if reversible $dW + de = 0$, since $dE = 0$ and $dS = 0$. Note that the non-conserved energy is considerable, being equal to the work done. If the process is irreversible,

$dE = dW + de$, where $de + dW$ is positive, since $dE > 0$ and $dS > 0$.

We have seen that the concepts of heat, work and entropy

must be defined organisationally. Heat and work are both solely macro concepts. Heat is the macroscopic, spatially non-directed transfer of energy (electromagnetic and gravitational) caused by symmetric interactions; work is the macroscopic spatially directed transfer of energy (of both kinds) caused by asymmetric interactions. The entropy of a system is a micro as well as a macro concept. It is defined as the measure of its *temporal* organisation, which is the probabilistic measure of the availability of its energy states. The entropy of a system evolves with time, as the probabilities of superposed states is a function of time; that is, states become available with changing probabilities. The entropy of a system is defined, mathematically, as $S = -k \log \sum p\varepsilon / \sum \varepsilon$ where ε is the energy of a state and p is its probability. We must return to the question of what it means for a particle to be organised and thereby discover the logical laws of quantum theory.

6

THE LOGICAL LAWS
OF QUANTUM THEORY

As an introduction to the logical laws of quantum theory, the concept of organisation must be defined. A set A is defined as organizing a set B if each element (member) of set A relates elements of set B. The organisation is the set which consists of the union of sets A and B. Set A is defined as the structure of the organisation. The structure may organise a plurality of sets. A particle is defined as a set of energetic wavefunctions organised by the set of properties of a point in space-time. It was proposed in thermodynamic theory that there are only two forces, electromagnetic and gravitational. Note that the answer has been obtained from thermodynamic theory! Since the photon is an electromagnetic wave, the logical law of symmetry can be applied if it is supposed that the photon and the neutrino both have zero invariant mass and charge and are the only particles for which this is true (gluons don't exist in our theory). It then follows, by symmetry, that the neutrino is a gravitational wave. This contradicts the Einstein general theory, which requires the spin of the graviton to be 2. This means the graviton does not exist. The experimental claim to have proven the neutrino rest mass to be non-zero is based on a tentative theoretical assumption. Since we seek a realist interpretation of nature, it is supposed that the wavefunction doesn't just carry information about the universe but represents a field of force. Since the photon and the neutrino are the only particles with zero mass and charge, all other particles will be assumed to have both an electromagnetic and a gravitational field and the wavefunction of the neutrino is a gravitational field. So all particles organise the combined electromagnetic and gravitational energy of their wavefunction (the photon combines electromagnetic with zero gravitational energy, the neutrino combines the gravitational with zero electromagnetic energy). This is in agreement with the proposed thermodynamic theory.

A particle is defined as an organisation, which is a point in space-time with a structural set of properties, relating a set of energetic wavefunctions representing combined gravo-electromagnetic fields. The realist interpretation of the wavefunction requires that the particle always has real properties, regardless of whether or not these are known or knowable. Are we then compelled to embrace the hidden-variable "naïve" realism of Einstein? No. Since this is a question about the nature of physical reality, to solve it, an appeal is made to the logic of reality itself: the ultimate (absolute) reality *is*, but is unknowable. So, analogously, the property of the particle in the superposed state must exist but is not only unknown but is unknowable, in principle. The property changes randomly. Not everything can be proven, not everything is knowable. Chance is written into the universe but, so too is determinism. The superposed state is then defined by its corresponding property being unknowable, that is, undefinable. This implies that the reduced state is defined by its corresponding property being knowable. This is so, as we shall see, but the implications of the particle being an organisation must first be examined. In the superposed state, the modulus of the square of the coefficient of an eigenfunction gives the probability of the particle having that eigenvalue at the time in question; but the value which it actually has at that time is unknowable. This is also the probability that the particle, were it to be in a reduced state at that time, would have that particular eigenvalue, which we shall later postulate as being a knowable state. The logical laws of quantum theory are innumerated

1. Energy is defined as the thing from which all real non-living things are formed.

2. A particle is defined as an organisation, which is a point in space-time, with a set of real properties, which organ ises its wavefunction. This is a set of linear superposed wavefunctions (eigenfunctions), defined by the space-time continuum.

3. The structure of a particle is defined as its set of proper ties. The identity of a particle is defined by its structure.

4. A set A is defined as organizing a set B if each element of A relates elements of B. The organisation is a set, which consists of the union of sets A and B. Set A identifies the organisation and defines its structure An organisation is identified by its structure.

5. The wavefunction is defined as a gravo-electromagnetic field.

6. There are only two forces, electromagnetic and gravita tional.

7. The universe has four real continuous dimensions, three of space and one of time.

8. The entropy of a system, micro or macro, is defined as the measure of its organisation in time, which is the probabilistic measure of the availability of its energy states. $S = -k \log \sum p\varepsilon / \sum \varepsilon$. k is Boltzmann's constant.

9. There is a logical law of causality: it is defined as the ordered pair (A, B); A implies B, of necessity. (B does not imply A, since the pair is ordered.) A is the cause of B.

10. An interaction, which violates T, causes a macroscopic change of entropy.

11. A particle does not interact with another particle if their wavefunctions superpose linearly, but does so when the combination is nonlinear.

12. A particle is in a superposed state if the corresponding observable is unknowable; a particle is in a reduced state if the corresponding observable is knowable. The prop erties of a particle are precise. They are precise and unde fined (unknowable) in the superposed state; and precise and defined (knowable or known) in the reduced state.

The wavefunction is a complex function which exists in Hilbert space. An observable is represented by an Hermitian operator. The state of a system is represented by a state vector. This is the mathematics of the Dirac-Jordan transformation theory. The list of twelve logical laws of the universe includes seven definitions which give physics an ontological foundation. These laws supplement logical laws, known since the early days of the evolution of quantum theory. These laws must be amended. The concept of measurement present in the latter, as stated by John Bell, must be eliminated, since an apparatus has no preferred role in nature; that is, a proposition cannot be a law of nature if it gives a measuring instrument a preferred role, since there is no law of logic to that effect. These laws are as follows: the wavefunction of a system represents the entire physical nature of the system; the law which states the Born probability interpretation of the squared modulus of the wavefunction for finding a particle at time t at position x; the probabilities of the outcome of a measurement of a system, in a superposed state, are given by the square of the modulus of the coefficients of the corresponding eigenfunctions; the Heisenberg uncertainty principle relating the limits of accuracy of measurement of conjugate observables such as position and momentum.

The Born probability interpretation must be taken to mean that the square of the modulus of the wavefunction is not only the probability of finding the particle at position x at time t, but is also the probability of the particle being at position x at time t, when the particle is in a superposed state. The squared modulus interpretation is the same whether the particle is in a superposed or reduced state. The law is, finally, restated so: if the wavefunction is in a superposed or reduced state, the squared modulus of the wavefunction is the probability of the particle being at x at time t. An experiment does not give the particle its property of position, it creates a definite position for the particle. But it does not require an experiment to achieve this. It can happen equally well outside a laboratory. This does not mean that the probability interpretation refers only to the reduced state. It refers also to the superposed state, in which position is also a real property but changes randomly, as determined also by the probability interpretation.

The next law has an analogous change. What is true for position is analogously true for any other observable. When a system is in a superposed or reduced state, the squared modulus of the coefficient of an eigenfunction, at time t, is the probability the system is in that state, at time t and has the corresponding eigenvalue. The concept of measurement is likewise unnecessary for the formulation of the Heisenberg uncertainty principle and is misleading and ambiguous. The principle is true whether or not a measurement is made. It is as true in the wild as it is in the laboratory. A particle, in the superposed state, since it is a real thing, must have real properties. They are not created by the act of measurement, though definite values of real properties can be so created. The principle must be interpreted as meaning that the range of possible random precise values of momentum determines—by the uncertainty relation—the range of possible random precise values of position and inversely. The principle expresses the range or breadth of unknowability. In the reduced state, the particle momentum is defined, that is it is knowable (or known), in which case the particle may be anywhere, that is, have any precise (undefined) value. If the particle position is defined, the momentum may have any of its possible precise (undefined) values. The reduction of the wavefunction does not require interaction with a measuring apparatus. There is no need to refer to a measurement in any of these laws. This achieves the aim of John Bell, who was, in my opinion, the most profound philosopher of physics of the latter decades of the twentieth century, to rid the formalisation of quantum mechanics of the concept of measurement.

Bell had two objections to the concept of measurement. The word intuitively carries with it the idea that we are measuring something which already exists, prior to measurement. Unknowable properties do exist prior to measurement. The act of measurement is a creative act, which creates a definite value, which did not previously exist. This gives the concept of measurement a new meaning. So there is real ground for Bell's concern about the ambiguity of the concept of measurement. However, concepts evolve and we must adapt to the new meaning of the concept of measurement. This objection of Bell's is not valid. His other objection, however, is so. The emphasis on the importance of measurement places classical systems in an ontological hierarchy above quantum systems, which is contradictory. All other concepts are ultimately subservient, in relation to reality, to sense-data. David Hume rises like a phoenix from the pyre of reductionism with Bohr's head tucked underneath his arm. This emphasis imprisons quantum theory in the solipstic madness of the Bohr-Heisenberg interpretation of quantum mechanics. Measuring systems are no different, physically, from any other. There is no ground for such preference. It is not enough to complain about solipsism. Quantum mechanics has to be radically amended and supplemented to rid it of this destructive philosophy. Law 12 will receive considerable discussion later, this being the law which marks the ultimate separation between classical and quantum theory.

From these logical laws, two structural laws have been deduced, in addition to the thermodynamic structural laws. These are 1) The wavefunction of the photon is an electromagnetic wave; 2) the wavefunction of the neutrino is a gravitational wave. In all other theories, the properties of a particle cannot be related to the nature of the particle but have to be `written in' from experiment; but in our theory they are deductively related. Since all mass has an energy equivalent, the mass of a particle is defined as the measure of its combined electromagnetic and gravitational energy. The invariant mass (rest mass) is the measure of the combined invariant electromagnetic and gravitational energy; the non-invariant mass is the measure of the combined non-invariant electromagnetic and gravitational energy. The property of (invariant) charge, which is the measure of invariant electromagnetic energy. The properties of mass and charge are the measure of the thing, energy. There are also properties that are measures of the motion of energy. The linear, angular and spin momentum are the measures of the linear, angular and rotational motion of the wave-energy of a particle.

There is no problem of the "infinities" in our theory. In classical, as well as in quantum theory, this problem exists: in classical theory, for example, the differential elements of charge, spread over a shrinking surface, tend to exert an infinite force. In our theory there is no such problem by reason of ontology: the charge is not a thing but a property of the thing, energy, which is spread over space. The wavefunction of energy cannot be reduced to a point since then the particle no longer exists (having no energy to organise). The problem of "infinities" cannot arise in quantum theory because a particle cannot have a definite position, except in a limiting sense.

All particles, except photon and neutrino, have both kinds of field; but not all have charge, that is invariant electromagnetic field: for example, the neutron has no charge; but it must have electromagnetic energy. So it has non-invariant electromagnetic energy and invariant combined electromagnetic and gravitational energy, in the rest frame of the particle, which is its invariant mass. In a frame in which the neutron is not at rest the measure of both kinds of energy combined is non-invariant; this being the non-invariant mass. The search for the magnetic monopole has proved as fruitless as the search for the Loch Ness monster. If a magnetic monopole did exist it could only mean, by definition, that there existed an invariant magnetic field. The only invariant electromagnetic field which exists is solely electric and not magnetic. The measure of this invariant electric field is the meaning of the electric charge. There is no magnetic charge, no magnetic pole, no magnetic monopole. Should you feel completely up the pole about this (as you may well do), you may rest assured it is not a magnetic pole.

The continuity of space and time is a logical necessity. That is the way the human mind thinks about space and time. Quantum theory does not require that space and time be grainy, that is discontinuous. The meaning of logical law 11 will be illustrated by explaining the meaning of inertia. This is at present attributed to the exotic Higgs boson, a mysterious yeti-like particle, (beardless by all accounts) which haunts other particles and fills the poor things with inertia. The only thing wrong with this hypothesis is the Higgs boson does not exist. The failure to find it has been to some extent blamed on the unavailability of the enormous energy required to find it rather than erroneous logic. To discover the meaning of inertia we must assume the truth of a covariant and metric determinant form of Newton's first law for microsystems, though Newton postulated the law for macro, not microsystems. An isolated particle, one which does not interact with other particles, jumps randomly from point to point of the wavefunction, always acted on by a force. The covariant form of Newton's laws are assumed to be true at the microlevel. Since it obeys Newton's first law of momentum conservation, the average force on the particle is zero, so it moves uniformly in a straight line. This means that a particle can never exert a self-force since, were the particle to be isolated, it would contradict Newton's laws, when expressed quantum relativistically. For the particle to change its motion, it must interact with another particle: the wavefunctions must combine nonlinearly. The particle resists with all its energy, that is, its entire mass, though the degree of nonlinearity will vary in space and time. This is the meaning of inertia: it is the resistance to a change in motion resulting from the creation of unbalanced forces produced by wavefunction interaction. Where there is no nonlinearity, as for photons, in vacuo, there is no inertia. There is no resistance to force because there is no force to resist. The concept of inertia is only valid if Newton's law of momentum conservation is valid; and if a particle does not exert a self-force. Otherwise the motion of a particle would change willy-nilly, and the nature of the universe would be fundamentally nondetermininistic. The universe is an interactive universe. Even in the nonliving world, there is a price to be paid for interaction. Particles don't like to be disturbed; if they are, they resist with every energetic element of their spatio-temporal organisation.

This explanation of inertia, a problem which Newton, Mach and others attempted to solve, suggests that we have been too quick to abandon Newton's laws, treating them merely as special cases of other laws. We will show that the laws of quantum logic enable the laws of Newton to be expressed in covariant, metric determinant form; that is the metric of macroscopic systems is determined by a contextual application of his laws.

7

THE QUANTUM RELATIVISTIC
FORM OF NEWTON'S LAWS

Let's turn our attention from the micro to the macrosystem. For an isolated macrosystem, accelerating relative to a linear (Euclidean) frame, there is the unexplained "fictitious", "magical", the so-called "inertial" force, which Newton attempted to explain by assuming the existence of an aether. The confusion in mechanics extended to electromagnetic theory. But Einstein could not explain the existence of the inertial force, which he correctly thought of as being gravitational. It has hung like a cloud over the physical landscape ever since, making it impossible to achieve a true general relativity theory. The time is ripe for a solution. The macro laws of Newton will be explained micromechanically, analogous to the macro laws of thermodynamics being explained micromechanically.

Let's not blame the stars, as did Mach, for the inertial force. The fault lies not in the stars, but in the system not obeying Newton's third law, the action-reaction law. That is, the blame for the "breakdown" of the first law is to be placed at the door of the "breakdown" of the third law. This would appear to contradict the assumption of Newton's laws being true. Since logical laws have been shown to be

91

valid only in context, analogously, since they cause structural laws, the latter are assumed to be valid only in context. But for what force is the third law to breakdown? Since there are only two kinds of force, it must be gravitational, since there is no inertial electromagnetic force. So, in nonlinear space, this force does not obey the first or third laws, only the second. Nonlinear space is then determined by the isolated system obeying the first and third laws, only for the electromagnetic, but *not* for the gravitational force. Since the inverse square law is assumed to be true it must be covariant and metric determinant, so the electromagnetic force (but not the gravitational), in nonlinear space obeys the law of inverse squares and so, of course, the law of momentum conservation also. Since in Euclidean space the inverse square law is obeyed by the electric force and charge is invariant, covariance requires that in euclidean space the mass which appears in the inverse square law for the gravitational force also be invariant; the charge, which appears in the inverse square law for the electromagnetic force in nonlinear space, is also invariant as required by covariance. The principle of equivalence cannot decide on this important question of mass and charge invariance and so cannot be true. Linear space is physically determined by momentum conservation of all forces, while nonlinear space is determined by non-conservation of momentum for the gravitational force. In linear space gravity obeys momentum conservation and obeys the law of inverse squares, while in nonlinear space gravity does not conserve momentum. As in thermodynamics, quantum theory is seen to be not just a theory of microsystems but also of macrosystems, the former explaining the latter. The electromagnetic force conserves momentum for both kinds of space but only obeys the law of inverse squares in nonlinear space. An isolated particle never produces a self-force but an isolated macrosystem does, in nonlinear space, because of momentum non-conservation of gravitational force. Energy conservation is replaced by a binary conservation-non-conservation law, momentum conservation likewise. Newton proposed the momentum law of macrosystems, for inertial frames only. Newton's laws are seen to be much more important even than we thought, since they alone determine the macro metric. See Tables 2 and 3. Newton's laws, as postulated by Newton, consisted of three laws of mechanics and an "orphan", the law of gravity. The law of gravity, because of inverse squares, seemed more akin to electromagnetism than to mechanics. This is a gift horse, inviting unification, which we have persistently looked in the mouth. Our theory incorporates gravity into the inverse-square law as the expression of this law in nonlinear space. Newton's laws must now be seen as the four quantum laws of mechanics which determine the macroscopic metric. The microscopic metric is determined by discrete symmetry violation as described earlier.

Table 2

Micro-Interactions

PROPERTY	CONSERVED	NON-CONSERVED
energy and entropy	for symmetric interactions in linear and nonlinear space	asymmetric interactions in linear and nonlinear space
momentum	for symmetric and asymmetric interactions in linear space for both kinds of force. For symmetric and asymmetric interactions for only the electromagnetic force in nonlinear space	for asymmetric and symmetric interactions, for only the gravitational force in nonlinear space

Table 3

Isolated Macrosystem

	Euclidean metric	Non-linear metric
static equilibrium	energy-entropy conserved; momentum conserved	energy-entropy conserved; momentum non-conserved
dynamic equilibrium (non-equilibrium state of classical thermodynamics)	energy-entropy non-conserved; momentum conserved	energy-entropy non-conserved; momentum non-conserved

8

THE QUANTUM-RELATIVISTIC
FORM OF MAXWELL'S LAW

If Maxwell's law is a real law of nature it must obey the law of general relativity; that is, it must be proven to be covariant and metric determinant. The vacuum is uniquely defined in our theory. Richard Feynman said that our ideas of the nature of the vacuum are unsatisfactory. Since there are only two forces, electromagnetic and gravitational. In our theory, the vacuum is uniquely defined as that state in which there exists no gravitational field. This is evidently the simplest premise as to the nature of the vacuum state and follows directly from the theory, without any ad hoc assumptions. Other definitions of the vacuum are ad hoc. In nature there always exists a gravitational field, so vacuum, like reversible process, is a limiting concept. The premise is made that electromagnetic fields only interact in the presence of gravity, so in vacuo, they only superpose linearly. By Newton's first law, the law of momentum conservation, light moves with uniform speed in a straight line in vacuo.

The Quantum Secret of Life

Maxwell's law says this speed is the universal constant c. Maxwell, like Newton, only constructed macroscopic laws. Maxwell's law is not a microscopic law about the motion of photons, of whose existence he was unaware, but a macroscopic law about the motion of light, which is a macrosystem of photons. You can see the macrosystem light; you cannot see the photon macrosystem. The second premise is made that electromagnetic and gravitational fields do not interact.

Maxwell's law states states that light (macrosystem) in vacuo moves with speed c uniformly in a straight line. The micro explanation of this is that photons in vacuo move with uniform speed c in a straight line. Since they only move with uniform speed, they have no inertia. The mass of the particle, which is a measure of its energy, is also a measure of its inertia, its capacity to resist a change in speed. But the photon does not change its speed so has no inertia and so no invariant or non-invariant mass. That is $m_0 = 0$ and $m_0/\sqrt{(1-v^2/c^2)} = 0$. For the photon the energy has no mass equivalent.

In linear space, *not* in vacuo, there is a gravitational field, in which case electromagnetic fields interact. Light does not move with speed c, but does move with uniform speed in a straight line, since by Newton's first law, electromagnetic momentum is conserved. But how do the photons move? The motion of the photons (microsystem) must explain the motion of light (macrosystem). Since the mass of the photon is zero it moves with speed c but since the photons interact, light moves in a straight line with a uniform speed less than c.

In nonlinear space, apply the law of general relativity, which Maxwell's law must obey if it is a law. Because of covariance, Maxwell's law, when relativistically expressed, says that light moves with uniform speed c, in a straight line, in nonlinear space. Photons are particles and so must obey Newton's laws. Electromagnetic fields interact in nonlinear space because of the presence of gravity. The electro-magnetic force obeys the inverse square law in nonlinear space as already proven. The inverse square law applies to the invariant mass, which is zero for the photon. So, although there is interaction between photons, the net force on the photon is zero and the photon moves in the same way as in vacuo even though there are forces acting. That is, a photon in nonlinear space moves with constant speed c in a straight line. So, light (the macro phenomenon which we may see with our sense of seeing) also moves with constant speed c in a straight line. This proves that the relativistic expression of Newton's laws establishes the relativistic expression of Maxwell's law, because it is covariant. It is obviously metric determinant because it enables clocks to be synchronised by light signaling with signals of known speed. The theory has deduced that Maxwell's law is a law. The law states that light moves with uniform speed c in vacuo and in non-linear space.

What then has happened to the classically enshrined concept that all systems possess inertia. The photon has no inertial resistance to a change in motion because there is no change in motion for it to resist. This means that the energy of the photon is not organised by the property of mass. A peculiar particle indeed. The photon is an eccentric particle, being the only particle which has only an electromagnetic field. As $v \to c$ for any massive particle the non-invariant mass, which is its inertia, tends to infinity. But for the photon the non-invariant mass does not tend to infinity but to zero! And m_0 is zero.

We must now discover the meaning of law 12 of quantum logic, a law that most strongly epitomises the ultimate and inexorable division between quantum and classical theory. Without it one might—as with David Bohm—maintain a philosophical bond with classical physics. With it the bond is severed and there cannot even be a tenuous link. Law 12 states that a particle is in a reduced state if the cor-

responding observable is knowable; a particle is in a superposed state if the corresponding observable is unknowable.

9

THE REDUCTION OF
THE WAVEFUNCTION

Relativity theory made an indissoluble link between subject and object (observer and observed). It made physicists ask the, till then, purely philosophical question, "What is reality?" For if a length is non-invariant it prompts the question, "Is it as real as a rest length which is invariant?" Ontology, the most important branch of philosophy, had entered physics with a vengeance and recast the philosophy of Locke in a most unexpected and disturbing way, by making what was formerly a primary, objective quality, a subjective, secondary quality, like those of sensory experience. The observer could not be left out of the physical equation and even threatened to become its most important ingredient. The rigid dividing line between objective physical reality and subjective consciousness had been crossed, for the first time, with dramatic and inexorable consequences. Quantum theory, heedful of its sister experience, took this large stride (a quantum leap!) forward by creating a subject: *created* reality. Physical reality cannot even exist except in so far as it is a subjectively *created* physical reality. This creative science is ideally suited to describe the creativity of life. Kant paved the way for this realisation a hundred years earlier but did not solve the problem of knowledge as he had thought.

The wavefunction was invented by Erwin Schrodinger, a cofounder of quantum mechanics, who thought that everything consisted solely of waves, whereas everything consists of particles, which organise wavefunctions. For the physicist the wavefunction is like a magic lamp. If you rub it, that is apply the appropriate mathematical operator for a given physical situation, it will conjure up a genie in the form of physical information about the system. If we rub the wavefunction the right way it may not be able to fulfil our wildest dreams but it does enable us to dominate the universe. Moreover, it can supply everything that can be known about the system. Schrodinger, like almost all physicists, regarded the wavefunction as a purely mathematical device which has the uncanny, indeed magical, ability to reveal a system's fundamental natural properties. How can a mere linguistic device, albeit mathematical, if not itself fundamentally related to the universe, penetrate its secrets other than by magic? Since we do not believe in magic, we propose that the wavefunction is physically real. The prejudice against this assumption has its source in the wavefunction containing the imaginary number i. This number is no less real than the natural number. The latter is a particular case of the former. All numbers are products of the human imagination but nonetheless real for being so and none are more or less real than others.

The mathematics of quantum theory is poker-faced, staring into a yawning abyss in which the union of subjectivity and objectivity is left wide open to philosophical speculation. The axioms of quantum theory are based on the mathematical object known as Hilbert Space. This space is unlike the space we experience in the macroscopic world, since it is by definition complex (imaginary). What objects live in this space? This is where quantum theory becomes inscrutable but only if you believe in magic. Let's remove the superstition from science. The wavefunction is a complex valued vector which lives in Hilbert Space. But our physical observables take on real values such as position, linear momentum, angular momentum and so on. So how does one make connections with this complex abstract world of wavefunctions and the real world? It is a premise of quantum theory that to every observable there corresponds a specific mathematical operator which acts on the wavefunction in a precise way. The outcome of this operation gives a probability expectation for the observable. This number is known as the eigenvalue of the operator. What has been explained can be beautifully described by perhaps the most fundamental equation in physics. The Schrodinger equation:

$$H \mid \psi \rangle = ih \, \partial \mid \psi \rangle / \partial t.$$

The speculations about the meaning of quantum mechanics have been weird and wonderful, outdoing science fiction. Neumann, aided and abetted by Eugene Wigner, attempted to solve the problem of reduction by a seeming madness, dragging in the concept most inimical to an observer-free science—consciousness. Ironically, while the other sciences were aping the observer-free master science of physics, with even psychology abandoning the concepts of mind and consciousness, physics was heading in the opposite direction. This was all the more comical in that physics was supposed to be the objective science par excellence, while psychology was supposed to be the opposite and, consequently, perhaps not even a science. Their attempt was defeated by the deafeningly paradoxical meowing of Schrodinger's cat which, even if only "half alive" still manages to keep a mocking grin on its face. So there's the prince of dilemmas; we must incontrovertibly tie the logic of quantum theory to the logic of cognitive consciousness since the evolution of physics, especially quantum theory, demands it; but what is the psycho-physical *reality* of consciousness itself; and how is it to be introduced, convincingly, into the theory such as to resolve the

Schrodinger and other paradoxes? If consciousness is not real it can have no causal role in a realist theory; if it is, this reality can only be accounted for by a revolutionary kind of logic, the logic, no less, of life itself. Since Neumann and Wigner were on the right lines, let's go part of the way with them and assume, not that the reduced state is that in which the property becomes known, but that in which it becomes *knowable*. The superposed state is that in which the property is unknowable. Only a subtle change in a morpheme, but Einstein said that god is raffiniert (subtle, shrewd, canny). The theory will demonstrate that this minute change in perspective constitutes a major revolution, ushering in a unified science of logic, physics, biology and psychology. The change, though subtle, has immeasurable consequences. The evolutionary philosophical inversion, introduced by Kant, paved the way for the science of the last two centuries; but Kant could have had no inkling of its evolutionary consequences. First it is demonstrated that it resolves the best known physical paradoxes.

10

THE RESOLUTION
OF THE PARADOXES

The Motion Paradoxes of Zeno

It is generally considered that there are two important motion paradoxes of Zeno. These are the "race-course" paradox and the arrow form of the paradox. The first of these is not a paradox. A runner has to run a given length. Before running the whole length he must have run half of it. Then, before running the second half, he must have run half of that half.

An so on. The whole stretch is composed of infinitely many successive pieces, each of some length. But the runner cannot finish an infinite task. Yet he does run the given length. This is not really a paradox but a contradiction. In concluding that he cannot run the given length, we must also conclude that he cannot even reach the first half way point.

So the original premise that he can do so is contradicted by the conclusion. So we have "If A, then not A" which is a contradiction. The arrow paradox is, however a genuine and important paradox.

The arrow form of the paradox consists in asking the following question: "In any indivisible instant of its flight, is a flying arrow moving or at rest?" If the former, how can it move in an instant; if the latter, it is never moving, and therefore, is at rest. The question arises from a misunderstanding as to what is meant by motion. There is no such thing as motion in an instant. Motion is defined with respect to a change of spatial position during a time interval (which contains an infinity of instants, however small the time interval). A particle, at an instant of time, can only occupy a precise position. There is no possibility of defining motion with respect to an instant of time.

This does not mean the arrow is not moving at every instant of its flight, it means that motion is a relational concept. It may be that it is the relational aspect of existence to which Zeno was trying to draw attention. The assumption that the arrow is moving is a logical assumption. If we make the logical assumption that the flying arrow is at rest, this is contradictory, so that quantum theory should be able to explain the contradiction.

The assumption being made is that the "flying" arrow is a series of snapshot rest positions, which give the illusion of motion. The present theory resolves the paradox without difficulty. If the flying arrow is at rest, the momentum is always known definitely to be zero, not in any limiting sense, but precisely zero. So, by the Heisenberg uncertainty principle, the position of the arrow (though always precise) is always infinitely uncertain. The arrow could be anywhere, between plus and minus infinity, in which case its wavefunction extends from plus to minus infinity. This is impossible since the energy of the wavefunction would, then, be infinite. The apparent contradiction has been explained. A flying arrow at rest is a physical as well as a linguistic contradiction. Zeno's motion paradoxes pose a profound challenge to the wishy-washy nonsense of contemporary theory, which sees a particle as being "smeared" over space. The wave-function, the energy wave, does spread over space, but this is organised by a point-particle, defined as the particle which has a precise (but never a definite) position.

The Paradox of Interference

When coherent monochromatic light is passed through two narrow slits an interference pattern is produced on a screen placed behind them. This is easily explained, on the wave theory of light, as the result of wave superposition at the screen from the wave contributions, with regard to phase, from the light at both slits. But on the particle theory a paradox arises. Even when particles are passed through one at a time an interference pattern is produced: a single particle behaves not just as a particle but, paradoxically, also like a wave. The paradox is resolved by the present theory because the particle is a particle which organises a wave and so behaves as particle and wave. If one of the slits is closed, the interference is destroyed. If the particle were solely a particle it is difficult to see how the mere presence of the other slit, the one it does not go through, could have any effect considering it is too far away. If a particle detector is placed at one of the slits the pattern disappears. Why should a lack of knowledge of which slit the particle went through—a purely subjective phenomenon—determine whether interference is produced. The reason is that the universe is a universe of consciousness; human cognitive consciousness is inherent in the universe even at the lowest level of organisation, the particle level. The wavefunction of the particle reduces if knowable, as when the detector is present, so the pattern disappears. It must not be thought that an experiment is necessary to collapse a wavefunction. Before life existed, wavefunctions collapsed throughout the universe if the particle state was knowable.

The Paradox of the Particle in a Box

This paradox unfortunately tends to be neglected, no doubt because it is so unfavourable to the Bohr interpretation. It is most instructive. Suppose a particle, A, to be anywhere in a box which has a central partition, which can be operated, such as to divide the box into two equal sections. At first suppose A to be anywhere in the box, so the wavefunction is finite for all positions in the box. When the partition closes, A can only be in one half of the box, yet on the Bohr interpretation, A has no definite position until it is observed, so it is not definitely in the right side or the left side of the box; that is, the wavefunction has not collapsed and hence all positions are possible. Clearly, on any realist interpretation of the particle, this is contradictory and the Bohr interpretation is nonsensical. In this realist theory, the wavefunction is reduced because the position is knowable, although no observation has been made. Not *known*, only *knowable*.

Suppose one half of the partitioned box is removed a great distance from the other half and an observation discovers the particle to be in a particular half of the box. On Bohr's theory the observation causes the wavefunction in the other half to disappear, however far apart the sections of the box may be. A causal influence (poltergeists?) without entanglement (because only one box contains the particle) has travelled at infinite speed, which is impossible. In the present theory there is no problem: before the separation, the wavefunction was already collapsed because its position was knowable, so the separation of the sections alters nothing and there is no mysteriously inexplicable causal influence.

The Wheeler Paradox

This is a fascinating paradox and a good illustration of the power of the resolution. After the photon has passed through the first half-silvered mirror there are two possibilities: (a) it is a one-path photon and (b) it is a two-path photon. If (a), the experiment is such as to make the path knowable as soon as it leaves the first mirror. The paradox arises if, after the photon has left the first mirror, the experiment is changed to produce an interference effect by introducing a final half-silvered mirror which produces a phase difference of a half wave length between the reflected and transmitted beams. Since the photon is always found to comply with the apparatus, as if it had read the experimenter's mind, it now becomes a two-path photon, so it would appear to have rewritten its own history. How can it change from a one-path to a two-path photon when it has already crossed the rubicon on leaving the first mirror. No problem. It is true that the photon, if its state is knowable, starts as a one-path photon, but, with the rapid substitution of the interference set-up, its state becomes instantly unknowable, so it changes, instantly, en route, to become a two-path photon. The state always instantly conforms to experimental alteration, however often a change is made. (You can't catch a particle napping, they're too smart.)

The Paradox of Schrodinger's Cat

This is the paradox which, originally, set the cat among the quantum pigeons. A cat, in dire contravention of animal rights, is placed in a box with an atom in a radioactive state. If the atom decays, it triggers the release of a fatal dose of poison, killing the cat. According to quantum mechanics, the state of the cat must be linked to the two possible states of the atom, so it is in a combination of alive and dead states until the box is opened when it can safely be pronounced dead or alive with the collapse of the wavefunction. The paradox has proved intractable, yet its solution could hardly be simpler. As Schrodinger suspected, the cat system cannot be linked to the atomic system: the cat is always in a knowable state. In principle, you can always determine the state of the cat, but not so the atom, which is in a superposition of states, so its actual state, until it collapses, is unknowable. The two systems, cat and atom, cannot be combined. The same criterion applies to Wigner's friend, or the infinite cascade of observers, each observing the other: the state of the cat, whether dead or alive, is always knowable, with or without observers; it makes no difference whether there is one, two, etc., observers, or, indeed, none at all.

The resolution of these paradoxes lends considerable support to the theory. Opinion in the twentieth century about reduction has been, historically, divided into the objectivist realist stance of eastern Europe, as opposed to the nonrealist subjectivist stance of western Europe. The truth is neither, but a synthesis of both: it is both realist and subjectivist. Max Born said it was possible there was truth on both sides but he was won over by the Copenhagen school of thought. "Knowable" means conceptually knowable. The reason why it cannot be an *act* of consciousness which reduces the wavefunction is because real systems were reduced before living beings even existed. Being knowable does not require the presence of an act of consciousness or of an observer. There is no longer any distinction between objective-real and subjective-unreal since it will be seen later that an experience symbolises reality, that is, experiences are real. The objective-subjective distinction is now between that which exists independently of experience (for example, the planet Mars) and that which is experience dependent (for example, the feeling of hunger). With the knowability condition for collapse, however, it looks as though we have jumped from pan to fire: for reduction to have happened only if the state was knowable, implies that man was predetermined in the universe, even when only particles existed. Predeterminism has for long been regarded as an outworn religious doctrine though physicists usually regard the world as evolving in obeyance of definite discoverable laws. Darwinism, however, sees the biosphere as being a purely contingent evolution with no all-embracing laws (except the law of evolution); and sees physics as having nothing of substance to contribute to the history of life, since particles are too simple to provide an explanation for anything so complex as life. Physicists, with their undue emphasis on chaos instead of organisation, and with their neglect of context, as Ian Stewart emphasises, have only themselves to blame for this. The current view is that even if the non-living world is, or could be, evolving according to a law-governed determinism, the living world, and hence cognitive consciousness, certainly is not. (See the books of Gould, Dawkins, Monod etc.) This would seem to make nonsense of the knowability condition even though it solves the quantum paradoxes. It is supported by the anthropocentric principle which says that the evolution of the universe is such that it must produce observers who are able to observe its evolution. The universe is, of necessity, and not merely by chance, a self-observing universe. The implication of the theory is that this cognitive explanation of reduction is not just a philosophical point of view but a quantum scientific logical law. This book must be confined to proving that the universe did evolve *deterministically* to produce noncognitive consciousness at the origin of life. This is done for cognitive consciousness in a following theory. Before doing this, the microscopic condition for the reduction of the wavefunction must be found now that the macro condition, knowability, has been discovered. From this will follow the first constructive quantum theory of atom and molecule.

11

THE MICROSCOPIC
REDUCTION OF THE WAVEFUNCTION

A physical interaction is represented by its Schrodinger equation. The eigenfunction solutions represent interactions for which energy is conserved so they correspond to the symmetric interactions of our theory. The superposed state of interaction must then be an asymmetric interaction. This is energy non-conserved and causes asymmetric and symmetric interactions. Since it causes symmetric interaction, this proves that the superposed wavefunction must reduce; it also proves that the eigenfunction must acquire asymmetric terms in the course of its evolution since otherwise asymmetric interactions could not be caused. The resulting asymmetric interaction, in turn, reduces to an eigenstate, which evolves to produce yet another asymmetric interaction with superposed states and so on. Such, in brief, is the endless merry-go-round of the world's microevolution.

Can we discover from the theory whether the universe had an origin? In our theory the question of an origin does not arise because neither reality can be said to be, nor the universe be said to exist, independently. Logically, you can't have one without the other. Since reality is unknowable, the question of the knowability or otherwise of the origin of the universe is unanswerable. The universe is a universe of energy. All energy is organised into particles. Particles must interact and do so according to the law that asymmetric cause asymmetric and symmetric interactions. If the universe has an origin, there would have to be a first asymmetric interaction, but this would have to be caused by a preceding asymmetric interaction. That is, there would have to be an endless causal chain, which contradicts the initial premise of the existence of an origin. So this conclusion as to the structure of the universe agrees with the logic of the universe, as expressed in terms of the concept of reality, which also says that the concept of an origin of the universe is contradictory.

When the superposed function evolves, it does so reversibly and deterministically; different eigenstates vie for predominance with ever-changing fortunes which follow the roll of the die (contrary to Einstein's naive realism). It is clear, by analogy with the evolutionary problem of thermodynamics, that when the collapse occurs, the process, at that instant, has discontinuously become irreversible and therefore violates T; that is, the superposed function violates T. Many eigenstates may be called but only one is chosen - but not by god, since not even god can influence the purely contingent final toss of the die; the outcome is ruled by the fickle goddess of chance and she alone. While the relation between interactions is causally deterministic, the reduction of the wavefunction is a purely chance phenomenon, occurring at an unpredictable instant. Here is the truly dramatic dividing line between classical and quantum physics. It is not just the root existence of chance, which is so shocking, it is the manner in which chance comes about. There is nothing remotely comparable to this discontinuity in classical physics. The wavefunction suddenly and, in principle without cause, collapses to produce a knowable definite value which is no more deserving of recognition than any of the others. The goddess of chance has the final word. To postulate that there is a god (not a goddess!) which knows, or could know, the ultimate reason for the existence of chance is to postulate an, in principle, knowable reality. This is contradictory. (Such a god would have to have the universal human attribute of cognition). The universe exists, for the most part, in a limbo of unknowability. Every now and then it jumps forward, unpredictably, into a state of knowability. Einstein was correct in insisting on the existence of determinism but not an unalloyed noncontextual determinism; Bohr was correct in insisting that chance existed physically, in principle, but not on its exclusivity.

The theory explains the uncertainty of the Heisenberg uncertainty principle: in the superposed state, that of the asymmetric interaction, the energy uncertainty is the measure of the non-conserved energy of the interaction. Likewise, momentum uncertainty is the measure of momentum non-conservation. A particle is real whether it is in a superposed state or in an eigenstate, so it has a set of precise real properties in both states; but, in the superposed state, these properties are unknowable, that is, undefined, changing randomly; while in the eigenstate, they are knowable, that is, defined. The superposed state collapses because the wavefunction violates T at some unpredictable instant. This T violation causes an irreversible change of entropy in the macrosystem, that is a change in properties which is knowable. This is the relation between the microscopic reduction of the wavefunction and the macroscopic irreversible change which it causes.

In Bohm's theory, which is also realist, following de Broglie, the particle is moved around by a pilot wave. It regards the unknown as not unknowable but as arising purely from a lack of information, so it is naively realistic. The theory, by resorting to a mystical form of holism, renders the universe incomprehensible in principle, so that physics becomes a lame duck. The pilot wave makes the wavefunction secondary, a distinctly retrograde step. Since there is no asymmetry, there is no reduction. David Deutsch is correct in exposing it as essentially a many-universe theory. It merely poses as a one-universe theory. Deutsch insists that a many-universe interpretation of quantum mechanics is the only true one. This is to misunderstand the true nature of deductive science. If it were true, it would be another logical law of the universe, not a structural law. A logical law cannot be deduced by causal implication - it is uncaused. The test of the a priori truth of a set of such logical laws is whether a set of universal structural laws can be deduced from them. Deutsch makes no such deduction, yet insists we have faith. Sorry, we believe in Santa Claus, Deutsch believes in Everett, whom he plainly considers to be the Everest of quantum theory.

12

A QUANTUM RELATIVISTIC
THEORY OF ATOM AND MOLECULE

The theory cannot be analytical, it must be synthetic or constructivist, since we wish to construct the evolution of the universe. As a first step, the particle has been defined as an organisation. The symbolist philosopher Ernst Cassirer, said that invariance is the key to the real; it makes possible the description of structure. Since consciousness must be structurally defined and the huge molecules of life are immensely structured, this implies that structural invariance must play a large role in the theory. Chemistry is only marginally unified with physics, that is with quantum theory, since chemistry is largely concerned with structure; yet quantum theory has nothing to say about structure. It has been known, for a few decades, by physicists, that asymmetric terms must be introduced into the Schrodinger equation, but the context in which such terms appear has not been understood. In our theory, there is no difficulty in answering this. To find out, we must define atom and molecule. They are assumed to be organisations. What is the nature of the asymmetric interactions which construct them and how are they related? A particle has a property structure, which organises the wavefunctions of the superposition and identifies the particle; these properties may be invariant or non-invariant under GCT. But atoms and molecules cannot be identified by non-invariant relations, the relations must be invariant under GCT. In the absorption and emission of a photon, the process, being reversible, there is no entropy change, so the asymmetric interactions which construct an atom do not violate T. But molecular construction does change the temporal organisation of the world, so the asymmetric interactions which construct a molecule do violate T. So, for the atom, interactions violate C and P but not T, while for a molecule, interactions violate CP and T. Molecules can be formed in two distinct ways: we postulate: by C violation as in electrovalent (ionic) bonding, when there is electron transfer; or by P violation, when there is electron sharing, as in covalent bonding. Covalent bonding produces spatial structures. Energy non-conservation is in some cases very slight, as in the case of radioactivity in the first case of violation (C and P but not T), and virtually undetectable by present day technology. An atom is defined as a set of invariant (under GCT) structural charge and spatial relations which organise a set of causally related interactions violating C and P but not T. They are causally related because they are asymmetric. A molecule is defined as a set of invariant (under GCT) charge or spatial relations which organise a set of causally related interactions violating CP and T. Since nucleic acid interactions are reversible, molecular violation of this kind (T violating) cannot, by itself, produce the origin of life. This falsifies the reductionist claim, repeatedly expressed by J.B. Watson (co-discoverer of the structure of DNA) and others, that the familiar laws of chemistry and physics of non-living matter are sufficient to explain life. (This philosophy might be termed "There is nothing new under the sun".)

Evolution required another violation: this could only be CPT violation, since god's alphabet contains only three letters. CPT violation, as we shall see, can occur in two ways: C or P, separately, but not T; and all of C, P, T, separately. In

Einstein's theory the absence of nonlocality forbids the violation of CPT, but nonlocality is now known to exist, so we are free to posit CPT violation. So important is this postulate that it would be no exaggeration to say that if the age of Newton ended with special relativity, the age of Einstein ended with CPT violation. Do both these ways occur in prebiotic and/or living systems? Does either of them occur in nonliving systems? What are the possible structural relations that can exist in either case? Before these crucial questions can be answered, we must validate the definitions by producing a quantum-relativistic theory of atomic construction; resolve the EPR paradox, which is essential for a theory of the origin of life; and complete the quantum theory of the nonliving world by relating quantum theory to the so far incomprehensible theories of classical mechanics and thermodynamics.

A Quantum-Relativistic Theory of the Atom

An atom is defined as an organisation which is a structured set of invariant (under GCT) charge and spatial relations between causally related interactions violating C and P but not T. For simplicity and convenience, consider a hydrogen atom in the ground state, $|0\rangle$. This is an energy conserving eigenstate which is metastable. The absorption of a photon is an asymmetric interaction which is a superposition of $|0\rangle$ and the first excited state, the eigenstate $|1\rangle$. It is reversible, that is, it does not violate T. This asymmetric interaction causes a symmetric and an asymmetric interaction. The symmetric interaction is the energy conserving eigenstate, $|1\rangle$, caused by the reduction of the superposed function. Being unstable, this state evolves into the energy non-conserved superposition of the eigenstates $|1\rangle$ and $|0\rangle$. This superposition is the caused asymmetric interaction. On reduction, the electron returns to the ground state, emitting a photon. The more non-conserved the energy, the shorter the life of the excited state. The non-conserved energy is a measure of the width of the state, being a measure of energy uncertainty. (It may be said that Heisenberg was certain about uncertainty but uncertain about certainty). The Schrodinger equation for the interaction does not violate T because entropy is conserved. The balance only applies to entropy and not energy, so atomic interactions cause work, that is change in spatial though not temporal organisation. The asymmetric interaction which produces radiation must cause symmetric and asymmetric interaction. The symmetric interaction is the ground sate, $|0\rangle$, the asymmetric interaction is the interaction of the emitted photon with another microscopic entity. The excited electron must return to the ground state because entropy is conserved; when the photon is absorbed the entropy (and energy) of the atom is non-conserved, so it must spontaneously emit a photon to restore the entropy (though not the energy) balance. This is the only theory that explains spontaneous emission and the existence of the energy width of a state. This is a major success of the theory. Though it is always tempting to take spontaneous emission for granted, since the time Bohr's original quantum theory, proposed it, it has never been explained and has been an abiding source of irritation, demanding an explanation. The return to the ground state is causally determined and must not be trivially explained away as a result of vacuum perturbation. From the definition of an atom, it follows that an atom need not be constructed of electrons, protons and neutrons, since there is no particle specification in the law. The reason the photon shows no directional bias in spontaneous emission is that the superposed function for emission does not violate P. The superposed function conserves T until it reduces, but it may or may not conserve C or P. In the case of stimulated emission, as in the operation of lasers, there is a directional bias in photon emission because the wavefunction solution for emission does violate P. It requires a population inversion to produce this. The way in which systems interact is determined by the nature of the symmetry violation of the interaction and the symmetry violation of the wavefunction solutions of the interaction. The theory explains why there is no anti*matter* (anti-atoms or anti-molecules), though antiparticles do exist. Because the interactions that construct an atom violate C and P, the charge reversed and space reversed interactions cannot be related by an invariant set of causal relations between the interactions. So there cannot exist an atom of antimatter. An antiproton may have a positron in orbit but there is no set of invariant charge and spatial relations between particle interactions.

13

RESOLUTION OF
THE EPR PARADOX

This paradox must on no account be seen merely as some irrelevant philosophical problem of quantum theory or the unearthing of minor faults in an otherwise workable and satisfactory theory. Rather it must be seen as throwing into sharp relief our lack of any deep understanding of the true nature of the theory. *Its solution provides the key to the origin of life.* Einstein produced a paradox among, as we have seen, an existing glut of paradoxes which had the paradoxical and ironic effect of rebounding with a resounding crash on his own special theory, not a quantum theory but a theory of relativity. If you question quantum theory, it takes it out on its sister relativity! He imagined a particle to decay into two particles which move off in opposite directions until they are a great distance from each other. The particles are in an entangled state, which means that the combined wavefunction is not a simple product of the wavefunctions of both particles, so that the properties of both particles are not independent of one another. The results of the measurements on both particles must be correlated. Momentum is conserved, so Einstein reasoned that if a measurement of momentum is made on one particle, a measurement of position made on the other simultaneously would give a definite value for *both* observables, simultaneously, contradicting the Heisenberg uncertainty principle which forbids such simultaneous definite knowledge. Worse, it also contradicts relativity, since the effect of communication of a definite value of momentum must have been communicated at infinite speed.

This nonlocality, which contradicted the Einstein philosophy of locality, was substantiated by the experimental test of the inequality theorem of John Bell, by Alain Aspect, in 1983. This was falsely interpreted as extinguishing all possibility of hidden variables. But Einstein was correct, though in a modified sense. Our theory shows that, in the superposed state, the property does exist—as Einstein insisted all along—and has precise, though not defined values. The values are unknowable, in principle, contrary to Einstein's "naïve" realism. So the lion of chance which gobbles up every concept which allows us to make sense of the natural world, lives peacefully, after all, with "hidden variables" and an objective physical reality. Einstein was not so much concerned with the exaggerated importance of the concept of chance, as its false implication that there was no objective reality. That it was all in the mind, as Bohr would have it. The paradox raises three major issues. Quantum theory and general relativity theory must be unified. What is the nature of physical reality? What is the meaning of nonlocality? This nonlocality question has haunted quantum theory for most of the last century. To solve it we must construct a new logical law of time-order relations between interactions. This is the fifth logical law of this new general relativity theory. It states: Interactions, which are causally related by particle transmission, have an invariant (under GCT) time-order relation, whereas interactions, which are not causally related by particle transmission, have a non-invariant (under GCT) time-order relation.

The correlations which exhibit nonlocality must be assumed to be causal since it would be inconsistent with a causally deterministic theory to do otherwise. The particles in question are in an entangled state and moving away from each other, so causation is obviously not by particle transfer. It was seen earlier that the wavefunction is a combined electro-gravitational field. It is, then, only the *energy* of the wavefunctions, organised by the particles, which is causally transferred and *not* the particles themselves. Since cause and effect, so related, have a non-invariant time-order relation, this transfer occurs at infinite speed in some reference frame, the one in which they are simultaneous. Causality is a logical ordering of implication, which may or may not also be a time-ordering relation; in this case it is not a time-ordering. In some frames cause precedes effect, in others effect precedes cause. Special relativity is not contradicted: this says that for events related by particle transfer there is an invariant time-order relation. But this transfer is not particle transfer, only energy transfer, so it does not contradict the law just stated. The assumed unreality of nonlocality, when Einstein was alive, led to the conclusion that CPT was conserved, but the resolution of the paradox allows us to assume CPT violation, opening the way, for the first time, to a theory of the origin of life. This will be pursued after the existence of classical physics has been explained.

14

THE MEANING OF CLASSICAL PHYSICS

Though we are all weaned on classical physics, its existence and nature are still not remotely understood. It has always been assumed to be a special case of quantum physics but it has never been understood in what sense this is so. In classical theory there is no asymmetry, nonlinearity or non-conservation. It must, therefore, limit itself to two diametrically opposite kinds of phenomena: (a) those of classical mechanics, in which there is no heat transfer and therefore no heat dissipation in a limiting sense, but mechanical work is done. (b) those of classical thermodynamics, in which there is heat transfer but mechanical work is done only in a reversible process, that is, in a limiting sense. The meaning of classical thermodynamics has been described previously. In (a), energy is communicated at infinite speed, in (b) the process is infinitely slow. For (a): If there were heat transfer, because heat moves randomly, there would be time for real asymmetry to evolve with the formation of superposed states with asymmetric terms, in which case, classical physics would not be valid; so that energy must be communicated at infinite speed. This can only happen by the communication of directed energy, that is, by the performance of work. Superposed states are formed but only in a limiting sense, collapsing the instant they are formed! The superposed state, which must cause work, acts just long enough to put in its quota of work causation. So the system appears to occupy an infinite number of successive energy conserved eigenstates. The process appears to be reversible because the system appears to spend all its time in an eigenstate. Non-conserved energy is balanced by the work it causes, as in the case of classical thermodynamics, so the concept of entropy is not necessary for classical mechanics, in which there is no heat formation. The observer who disturbs these states must make a correction for the disturbance. The assumption is made of ideal rigid bodies, which communicate energy instantaneously, in a reversible interaction, which exists only in an ideal sense. A classical system is in a permanently reduced state, punctuated by superposed states of "zero" time interval. The properties of the system are always knowable, always definable. This means that interaction, though it exists in a limiting sense, can be totally ignored. Classical mechanics looks backward in time to an ideal system, which it tries not to disturb; quantum mechanics looks forward in time to the creative result of disturbing the system, a result which cannot exist without the disturbance. It cannot be too strongly emphasised, for biologists as well as physicists, that the latter is ideally suited to express the purposeful, future-directed creativity of living systems. To offset the limitations of classical mechanics, classical thermodynamics was inevitably invented to account for systems engaged in heat transfer. In so doing we jump from pan to fire. If heat is transferred too quickly the process is irreversible, but classical physics has no concept of asymmetry. Without asymmetry no work is caused to be done. If the process is only slightly irreversible, the asymmetric non-T violating interactions produce almost balanced work (net work zero) and the only other work done is by the only slightly T violating interactions, the very interactions the "reversible" process hypocritically denies, both eating and having its cake. A real macro process is irreversible and must last a finite time. Classical physics is a conjuring trick which only works for specially selected phenomena, namely those for which asymmetry and non-conservation, always present in nature, can be ignored. Classical physics is what quantum physics does when it goes on holiday.

15

CPT VIOLATION

Since nonlocality is real, CPT violation is assumed. If a thing can happen in quantum theory, it eventually will. T alone cannot be violated, since such an interaction does not conserve energy or entropy; so this violation would cause a macrosystem to increase its entropy without causing work to be done. It was proven in the thermodynamics section that electromagnetic work is caused by C violation and gravitational work by P violation. T violation alone is impossible, since there can be no change in organisation in time without a change in spatial organisation in a real process. So T alone cannot be violated. There are just two possibilities for combined CPT violation: (a) C or P is violated or (b) C and P and T are violated. Evolution is a gradual, step by step (but not continuous) process. (You step upstairs gradually, one at a time, but not continuously; you don't stop at a fraction of a step.). The most plausible next evolutionary step is (a) not (b). It is more likely that evolution advanced from single and double violation to (a) than from such violations to (b), since the change to (a) requires a lesser degree of asymmetry. The ladder of progressive evolution of the universe with singleton, double and triple violation could hardly be more aesthetically pleasing. It is keenly felt that here at last lies revealed the ultimate secret of the origin of life. The simplicity is startling. The genetic code contains only four letters, yet the entire universe is coded by merely three letters, though the number of violations is still four. (One may ask, quizzically, if the letters A GCT, of the genetic code, are trying to give physicists a broad hint!)

What is the physical meaning of C or P violation? Since atoms and molecules are created, discontinuously, in sets, a solution is sought which is a discontinuity. Particles don't organise particles, atoms don't organise atoms, but molecules do organise molecules. So a new possibility has entered evolution: instead of qualitative discontinuity, we have quantitative discontinuity. The discontinuous creation is the formation of a macromolecule, defined as a molecule with discontinuously large entropy. Since ordinary-sized molecules are constructed from interactions which violate C or P, and T, the simplest postulate is that the new kind of interaction violated C or P but not T; that is, molecules were constructed for the first time from reversible processes, as is the case for atoms. (Recouler pour mieux sauter - one step back, two steps forward). It follows that the law of structural formation of a macromolecule is that it is formed with the creation of a set of invariant, under GCT, charge or spatial relations between causally related CPT violating interactions which violate C or P. See Table 4. This is promising, since living systems contain supramacromolecules: the law implies that they could be created if, instead of charge *or* spatial, we have both charge *and* spatial invariant relations. In prebiotic and living systems there are two, and only two, kinds of supramacromolecules: protein and nucleic acid. Since protein interactions are irreversible and nucleic acid interactions are reversible, the next evolutionary step is evident: a prebiotic system originates as an open system which contains *both* kinds of CPT violation (a) C or P; and (b) C, P, T. Interactions of type (a) create nucleic acid; interactions of type (b) create protein. See Table 5. Since causation results from asymmetry, the greater extent of the violation of (b) suggests that the evolution of protein caused the evolution of nucleic acid. This is also suggested by the inability of nucleic acid to replicate without the presence of protein. That this must have been so can be seen from the following: prior to the existence of a prebiotic system interactions between molecules caused interactions between molecules, but molecules never caused molecules (that is, interactions between things caused interactions between things but things never caused things); but in a prebiotic system, because of the addition of violation (b), (violation (a) already existed in evolution) molecular structure in a prebiotic system caused molecular structure (information caused information). So it is structural change produced by violation (b), which causes structural change produced by violation (a), and not inversely. This is a consequence of new evolutionary properties "emergent" as a result of the new violation (b). This would appear to be contradicted by the already existing presence of type (a) CPT violating molecular structures in abiotic systems; but we shall see that there are two crucial differences between this type of molecular structure in prebiotic systems as compared with abiotic systems. The prebiotic system behaves as a self-organizing open system, so analogies will be made between this system and the self-organizing isolated system. This is done first at the macro level, then the macro-level laws will be explained micromechanically. There must, of course, be a set of logical laws of life. The following observation about CPT violation will enable this to be done.

Table 4

ORGANISATION	SYMMETRY VIOLATION	STRUCTURE
1. particle	nonlinear superposition of a set of wavefunctions	point-particle with organising set of non-invariant and invariant properties
2. atom	separate violation of C, P, not T	a set of invariant charge and special relations between *causally* related particle interactions which violate C, P, not T. Interactions *reversible*
3. molecule	CP combined violation C or P; and T. CPT not violated	a set of invariant charge or spatial relations between *causally* related atomic interactions which violate C or P, and T. Interactions *irreversible*
4. marcomolecule of an abiotic system	CPT combined violation. C or P; not T	a set of invariant charge or spatial relations between *causally* related moleculare interactions which violate C or P; not T. Interactions *reversible*

Table 5

INTERACTIONS	MACROSYSTEM
1. symmetric	all systems, abiotic, prebiotic and biotic
2. C and P violated; not T	all systems
3. C or P violated; and T CP combined	all systems
4. CPT violated C or P; not T	abiotic systems only, in which there are macromolecules
5. CPT violated; all of C,P,T	only prebiotic and biotic

So far in evolution, we have seen in the structure of atom and molecule, invariant charge and invariant spatial relations between causally related interactions. Why are invariant time-ordered causal relations not part of the structure which identifies atom and molecule? The reason is that in the non-living world all causal relations, when causality is effected by particle transfer, have an invariant time-order relation. Things are not distinguished by whether or not they have invariant time-ordered relations any more than people are distinguished by whether or not they possess a head. This raises a fascinating possibility: suppose that, because of the intriguing novelty of the twin versions of CPT violation, at some advanced stage, say, in the evolution of a prebiotic system, there evolved, for the first time in the universe, *non-invariant* time-ordered relations between *causally* related interactions, analogous to the existence—in the non-living world—of non-invariant charge and spatial relations between causally related interactions. Analogous to the latter evolving to produce a thing (atom, molecule), at a higher level of organisation, with a set of invariant structural space and/or charge relations, it must follow that A new *thing*, at a higher level of organisation, is formed by a prebiotic system. This happens with the creation of a set of invariant time-ordered relations between causally related interactions, precisely because they *evolved* from *non-invariant* time-ordered relations between causally related interactions, which existed in the prebiotic system, preceding the origin of the biotic system. The resolution of the EPR paradox demonstrated that, even in the non-living world, non-invariant time-ordered relations do exist for causally related interactions, but only if the energy transfer is not communicated by particles (as in entanglement). It follows that, in the prebiotic and biotic system, non-invariant time-order relations between causally related interactions exist *even if the causal relation is communicated by particle transfer.* Different things were formed in the past, at successively higher levels of organisation, with the formation of new structures which are sets. It would be illogical to suppose that this new structure, a *set* of invariant time-ordered relations between causally related interactions, does not produce a still higher level of organisation. (If a thing can happen it will). Since the formation of invariant time-ordered relations clearly marks the origin of life, this new thing is defined as an experience. It does not relate to an object outside the biotic system, so it is named a "feeling". It is a set of invariant time-ordered relations, therefore it exists only in time and not in space. Since this new kind of thing exists only in time, the agency of causality cannot be force; it will be defined as selection (choice). Selection implies purpose. What is doing the selecting and for what purpose? We naturally assume the selection is made by a life, which is defined as a set of experiences (of feelings). A life selects non-invariant time-ordered relations between causally related CPT violating interactions, with the purpose of creating a *set* of invariant time-ordered relations between them, that is a new experience of feeling. A life evolves by means of this selection process, creating more and more new experiences. A life which cannot select, which ceases to exercise free-will, dies. Every living thing has free will and evolves purposively. But does it, even at the origin of its life, have consciousness? The ability of any organism to relate itself with permanence and stability to the universe and reality, can only be the result of the formation of invariant relations. So we define the structure of the experience, its *set* of invariant time-ordered relations, as its *consciousness*. The number of invariant relations in the structure of an experience is the measure of its consciousness. A life performs the functions of an organism by selecting the appropriate experiences, which provide the required sets of invariant time-ordered relations characteristic of any given process. It can select any experience in its set of experiences. The more life an organism has the more it relates to the universe and reality, that is, the more creative it is. So we assume the measure of consciousness of an experience is its magnitude, defined as the measure of its life. The more evolutionary advanced a life, the greater its ability to relate to the universe and reality. Life is defined, analogously to energy, as the only thing from which all experiences and lives are made. A life is a whole, a set (a "holism") which is constructed of the thing life. An experience of feeling is a life quantum, which is identified by its structure, which is defined as its consciousness. The measure of consciousness of an experience is the measure of its life; this is also the measure of the structural organisation of the experience. The measure of energy of a nonliving thing is the measure of its mass, so mass is analogous to consciousness and energy to life; but consciousness is also the measure of organisation of an experience (the measure of the thing is also its measure of organisation); whereas another concept, entropy, is needed to define the measure of organisation of a nonliving thing. With life, you get two concepts for the price of one! Experiences are real biophysical entities, because they are sets of invariant relations which are the structural properties of the experience. By a law of ontological logic, this means they are real things, constructed from the real thing which is life (analogous to the real thing, energy). Experiences are no less real than nonliving objects: the law of logic which defines their reality is one and the same. It is the life of the organism which constructs its structure and processes. Nucleic acid and protein do not construct themselves. It is the life of the organism which does so by the exercise of free will or selection. Just as forces bring about interaction between bodies, so selection brings about the evolution of the life of a cell. The logical laws of life can now be formulated.

16

THE MICROSCOPIC
ORIGIN OF LIFE

The Logical Laws of Life

Even as late as the nineteenth century it was generally considered that life is an insoluble mystery. Darwin thought that the origin of life could not be discovered, in principle, because it was a unique event of high improbability. During the twentieth century, opinion has veered in the opposite direction. Biochemists are convinced the origin of life can be discovered. But without a physical, unified quantum relativistic theory their efforts have been doomed to failure. What is this entity called life and how does one reason about it? To answer these questions we shall apply our theory of knowledge. This means we must begin by constructing a set of logical laws of life from which we shall deduce structural laws of living systems. The logical laws of life are as follows:

1. Life is the thing from which all experiences and lives are formed.

2. A life is an organisation, a set of experiences, structured by a set of invariant causal or acausal relations between the experiences.

3. A life selects non-invariant (under GCT) time-ordered relations between causally or acausally related supra macromolecular interactions, which violate CPT, with the purpose of forming a set of invariant (under GCT) time-ordered structural relations between these causally or acausally related interactions.

4. An experience of feeling is defined as an organisation, which is identified by a set of invariant (under GCT) time-ordered structural relations between causally or acausally related supramacromolecular interactions, which violate CPT.

5. The consciousness of an experience is defined as the set of its structural relations. An experience identifies itself with its consciousness, which exists only in time.

6. The invariant relations of an experience symbolise the universe and reality. Life and experience are real.

7. The magnitude of an experience is its measure of life, defined as the measure of its consciousness.

8. Experiences exist at different levels of consciousness, of which feeling is the lowest. The level of consciousness of an experience is defined as the hierarchical relation which it makes with the universe and reality.

9. Selection by a life is analogous to force as the agency of causation of experience.

10. Experiences and lives exist only in time.

The logical laws, which define organisation and causality, can be regarded as added to the list. Only a few additional laws are required as the theory evolves. From this set of laws of logic the macro structural laws of biotic systems are deduced by analogy with the quantum laws of thermodynamics.

The Macrostructural Laws of Biotic Systems

The so-called "non-equilibrium" state of an isolated system, of classical thermodynamics will be defined as an equilibrium state, a state of *dynamic* equilibrium since a physical parameter, entropy, is always increasing. The equilibrium state, of classical thermodynamics, since entropy is unchanging, is a state of static (thermodynamical!) equilibrium. There is no analogy to an equilibrium state for the prebiotic system. But there is, analogously, a law of unilaterally increasing *tendency* towards an equilibrium state because the system is self-organizing: it starts with ordinary sized molecules, develops macro, then supramacromolecules, and ever-increasingly evolved charge and spatial structures, ending with the temporal structure which converts it into a biotic system. Before the evolution of the prebiotic system, no open system was self-organising, only isolated systems were so. Analogously, this unilaterally increasing tendency must culminate in the creation of a state of dynamic equilibrium, that of a *biotic* system with a unilateral increase of entropy, a state of dynamic equilibrium. This is the *macro* physical condition for the origin of life:

A prebiotic system becomes biotic when its entropy, which has an increasing tendency towards unilateral increase, does increase unilaterally.

A prebiotic system has no purposive drive towards equi librium—it is not alive—but it is self-organising; this jus tifies the analogy with an isolated system.

The unilateral increase of entropy of a biotic system implies that the way to cross the Great Divide, the conceptual gulf which separates the living from the non-living, is to link the concepts of entropy and life. C or P but not T violation (type(a) of CPT,) on its own, cannot create *supra*macromolecules, since these molecules do not exist outside the prebiotic system. Yet nucleic acid is a supra-molecule, the product of this kind of violation. So there must be causation of nucleic acid by protein, resulting from triple separate violations of C, P, T. (type(b)). A change in protein function which is the formation of a new set of invariant *time*-ordered relations is a change in consciousness. This change in consciousness must then be the cause of a change in nucleic acid structure, that is, a genetic mutation. The latter change in molecular structure is a change in the molecular organisation of the system, that is, a change in entropy. Every change in consciousness is accompanied by a change in entropy. So a change in consciousness has caused a change in entropy. There is therefore a law of unilateral increase of life of a biotic system as well as a law of unilateral increase of entropy of a biotic system. The life of a human, for example, always increases from cradle to grave. The life of a system increases its measure of life by creating new experiences, each of which causes a genetic mutation and, in so doing, increases the entropy of its body. The unilateral increase of entropy is an inevitable consequence of the unilateral increase of life. Life and entropy are allied concepts. From the origin of life in a biotic system there is a unilateral increase in the organisational development of the body and life of the organism. The first being caused by the second. Life is a one-way ticket. No matter how many experiences may be rejected or forgotten there is always an increase in the acquisition of bodily properties and life. Even old age, apart from illness, does not halt this advance.

Strange as it may seem, a living system is not so unlike an isolated system after all. One could even say that a living system is a special kind of open system which has learned the trick of parodying an isolated system, thanks to the possession of a special kind of violation. The success of this analogy suggests a further analogy. An isolated system always reaches a state of static equilibrium, a state of maximum entropy. Analogously, the law which states the purpose of life is that the life of a biotic system always selects such as to maximize its life as a whole. This is the law which governs its stability. If it ceases to obey this law, the laws of unilateral increase are not valid for the system, the organism ceases to evolve and dies. When the spirit—that is the urge to live—goes, an organism no longer tries to maximize its life and dies. It is a holistic law. Its meaning is that the life of every organism must reach for the stars, within its capabilities and limitations. Even when an organism chooses to compromise, it does so in such a way as to maximize its life as a whole. This proves that the unsatisfying philosophy of utilitarianism is false. This states that the purpose of life is the creation of the maximum happiness for the greatest number. (Happiness is not a scientific concept.) If inflicting harm makes most people happy and gives them the maximum pleasure does this mean we should encourage cruelty. This could only be a human law, denying the possibility for a general law, valid for all organisms. Are microbes, beetles, and flowers happy? The boy who is set on being an astronaut will abandon his dream if the law requires him to do so. He creates the dream in order to maximize his life but may also abandon it for the same reason. However subtle and varied and complex may be the immediate aims of our behaviour, the overall and over-riding motivation is simple and always the same: maximization of the life as a whole. An organism may risk the necessities of life (food, safety, shelter) or, paradox indeed, life itself (mountaineer, explorer, test pilot) for this end.

In Darwin's theory mutations happen purely by chance, with the development and behaviour of the organism having no influence whatsoever on the hereditary genes; those mutations which are best adapted to the environment leave most descendants. The hypothesis of natural selection makes only a negative statement about mutations: they are not caused by the living process of the organism. So what causes them? By implication they are uncaused, they just happen—ours is not to reason why. Which means that life is inherently incomprehensible; yet Darwinists claim to be *explaining* evolution. The only causality they allow is between the environment and mutation. This has the unfortunate effect of bypassing the organism, making its development irrelevant as a causal agent of evolution.

Richard Dawkins, a foremost proponent of "fundamentalist" Darwinism, is correct in metaphorically describing the organism as merely the "vehicle" of the genes. The organism is conceptually trivial since it only appears in the theory in a statistical sense. Dawkins doesn't know he is the little boy who sees the emperor has no clothes, because he likes the emperor not to have any clothes. It is not entirely a mechanistic theory as is claimed (as if that were a recommendation), since an organism adapts for the purpose of survival. Survival is not the primary purpose of life though it is, of course, necessary if the primary purpose of maximization of life is to be achieved. If survival were all, altruism could not exist. The reason for human altruism is idealism, a way of maximizing life by reason of the satisfaction gained from the finer qualities of feeling and sensibility which they bring to life by promoting human values and social relations. Altruism has, granted, an impact on the genes but to place the gene before life is to place the cart causally before the horse. Having causally written the individual out of the evolutionary process, it is explained by uncaused mutations, which are caused to reproduce, differentially, by the environment. This divorces ontogeny from phylogeny (that is, the development of the organism from the development of the species), which is illogical. This essentially causeless, purposeless, illogical mechanism is held to be responsible for the transparently purposeful, deterministic, immensely organised evolutionary biomechanism that is the biosphere. How do you build the Eiffel

Tower? Well, you just take lots of scrap metal, bang the bits together any old how, go to church and pray to the almighty -obvious, ain't it? Evolution, as a purely chance process, denies the possibility of progress -it is merely a history, a recording of events. The attempt, by heretically inclined, forward-thinking Darwinists, to substitute the concept of complexity for organisation, only serves to heap confusion upon illogicality, though it is an error in the right direction.

The macroevolution of the present theory implies a very different micro explanation of evolution from that proposed by Darwinism. A new experience, if it is to play its part in maximizing the life as a whole, must cause a favourable mutation in the body of the organism, otherwise it could have no lasting effect on its life. Darwinism has no answer to what causes a favourable mutation and cannot even identify a single favourable mutation (only neutral or unfavourable mutations). *This, of itself, is sufficient to invalidate the selectionist hypothesis.* For Darwinists, favourable mutations are purely chance mutations: the life of the organism has no role in their creation. This is a logical premise but they make no deductions about the structure of life to support the premise. They do not know what life is, they cannot define it, and regard the origin of life as a purely chance phenomenon beyond explanation. They are reduced to reductionism, the belief that the familiar laws of physics and chemistry are sufficient to explain life. We have seen that living systems require a new logical system, logic of life, and that a new kind of physical violation, in which all of C, P and T are separately violated, defines the origin of a prebiotic system. Darwinism does not even begin to face up to the question of Descartesian dualism of life and body. Purpose in Darwinism, survival through competition, could be replaced, logically by any other purpose, for example, survival through co-operation, instead of competition, without any effect on the theory, though the selected purpose would give rise to a different just so story to account for what constitutes a favourable mutation. All that ultimately matters in Darwinism is chance mutation being (metaphorically)"selected" by the environment. The selection is, of course, not real. Modern biological science being new (yes, new), biologists have not yet learned that on no account should one introduce metaphor, a purely literary device, into the expression of a law. This is sufficient to invalidate the law. Metaphor is useful in the explanation of a law but must not enter the law itself. This is not to deny the obvious existence of competition; but, as Brian Goodwin says (in *How the Leopard Changed its Spots*), competition is secondary, it does not have a primary role in evolution. Darwinism is only a one-way deterministic theory since the arrow of causal determinism always points from gene to organism, never from organism to gene. This means that we are no more than biogenetic robots, at the mercy and bidding of our genes, with the way we conduct our lives having no influence on the evolutionary process. Mindless, soulless, spiritless, wholly probabilistic, in effect purposeless and nondeterministic, Darwinism. It claims to explain the overall process of evolution, a theory of biology (bios = life), yet excludes life, the real thing, entirely from the process. It has spawned, in its wake, conditioned reflex knee-jerk determinism (reputed to have been created by jerks, yet Darwinism is a theory of continuous evolution!); a theory infamous for reducing man to "ratomorphic" man. At least rats are alive. Richard Dawkins, scrupulously following the letter—if not the spirit—of the original Darwin theory, reduces us to a lifeless spirit or zombie; a slave to our genes as well as our "memes". Reeling under the onslaught of the redoubtable philosopher Mary Midgely, Dawkins, with a dexterous, swift, reverse double somersault, on the high-wire of fundamentalist Darwinism, deftly outflanks us by claiming that what he really meant is that robots, consciousness or no, are already supremely versatile and intelligent beings, capable, in time, of ousting man from his evolutionary perch. We should feel flattered to be compared with robots whose screws we are not fit to polish.

The real cause of mutation is consciousness. A true blue life-pensioner reductionist, Dawkins thinks consciousness conceptually irrelevant to biological evolution. As the concept of consciousness thrust itself to an ever-increasing degree into the consciousness of biologists—and all the best people were climbing aboard the consciousness wagon—Dawkins, with commendable intellectual integrity, at last deigned, albeit reluctantly, to acknowledge its existence, but only to admit he had no idea as to its meaning. Dawkins, and his biological twin, John Maynard Smith, used to maintain that consciousness was merely a distraction from the mainstream of science. Dawkins sees himself as an avant-garde scientist, but though a lucid and distinguished writer and a jaunty antagonist in the field of biology, he is a scientific reactionary. Give me that old-time, Victorian, undilutedly mechanistic, shiny and polished Darwinism with a "selfish" twist: there is no society, no hierarchical levels, no unholy holism, no consciousness, (almost) no Darwin, only the individual gene; which does, yes, co-operate with other genes. But even that co-operation is ultimately just a subtle form of selfishness. So when "Dawkin has finished his squawkin'" all we are left with is Evil, evil, evil - evolution is inescapably evil, heaven forfend (let's call it evilution instead). Thank goodness, the Lord, in his mercy, has sent us his only everlasting, uniquely unselfish son, Dawkins, the computerised robotic programme, Dawkins Dawk, or is it Doc Dawkins, who has been inspired enough to warn us of our original sin and to propose a memetic cure, which he says only requires belief in a free will he says we robots don't have. Richard Dawkins, the self-appointed pinnacle of evolutionary morality—as he so unerringly plumbs the depths of our fathomless gullibility and naivete—commands our undying gratitude and unstinting admiration. His sacred message is that the entire purpose of genes is to go forth and multiply. But aren't genes just molecules and molecules don't have purpose? Never mind, why spoil a good metaphor (or a good yarn), the existence of purpose is logical; so let's take purpose away from man and organisms in general and give it to the genes; a state of confusion which produces two ferociously hostile armed camps: genetic determinists such as Dawkins and Dennett and no less determined genetic indeterminists such as Gould, Rose and Lewontin. The road to hell is paved with Darwinist aphorisms and mantras.

Our society is a scientific society. The scientists of the western democracies, with an emasculated Kantian philosophy, have vied with the, not accidental, political dictatorships of the twentieth century in destroying the concepts of freewill and the spirit of man. How can robotic man have morality? What is morality anyway, say Darwinists, but a subtle form of selfishness; isn't it better to expose the sham of morality for what it really is. A. J. Ayer, a reductionist ad absurdum philosopher and positively, a positively illogical logical positivist, said that morality is merely an expression of emotion. Darwinism does not deny the existence of morality but has spawned some strange philosophical bedfellows. To deny that society is governed by meaningful, moral laws, borders on the inane, some would even say the insane. Dawkins, a humanist, who, analogous to the gospel of love, proposes a biological gospel of selfishness, not surprisingly hates religion, though he does not deny the importance of morality; but he sees it as having no bearing on scientific explanation. Moral or cooperative behaviour is just one more card in the competitive game. Dawkins invites us to choose between the profundity of religious myth and his own tawdry and infantile memetic myth. He declaims, with a fervour that Saint Paul would have envied, that we alone (with the help of Dawkins, of course)) can overcome the selfishness of our genes and defeat wholly selfish genetic determinism. A stirring and passionate evangelical message, to be sure. But what does it really mean? Dawkins, not so blind as some, is correct in insisting on the cultural discontinuity of man's evolution, but as usual with Darwinism, we have no biological explanation of this discontinuity and so no explanation of man's origin. Man, even if he is the paragon of animals, is an eccentric and therefore biologically unimportant. Analogously, the physicist thinks that asymmetric interaction is a side issue, marked only by radioactive decay. But it is the entire universe which is asymmetric in its interactions. So, also, all biological evolution is governed by consciousness. Man alone has a self-conscious consciousness because only man knows laws, has culture and therefore has speech to express his consciousness. If Dawkins is really so confident about his memetic message why does he not take it to its inevitable logical conclusion and admit that man's stay in the universe may not be transitory after all and may be indefinite if we win out against our genes. The reason he does not is that he is afraid that he has opened Pandora's box. The meme of free will and consciousness is about to stick in his gullet. Dawkins has been bypassed by the mainstream of progress in biology. This now depends on the advance we make in our understanding of the concept of consciousness. Humphrey, Dunbar and others have been making some progress in that direction. The waters of the dam of consciousness are now about to burst upon the hapless Dawkins. The perceptive will see his curiously inept and illogical invention of the meme as a last despairing rearguard action to save him from toppling from his high wire. But the Kuhnian flood will sweep away the phlogistonian flag wavers Dawkins, Dennett, Smith and all their motley crew of fundamentalist neo-mafia biological determinists. A new biology will emerge from the flood, one unified with the other sciences, in all of which consciousness has a key role. The immaturity of biological science is accurately described by Jeremy Campbell in *Grammatical Man*:

"Biologists are [similarly] baffled, despite the immense abundance of recorded facts at their disposal. They have not succeeded in describing the living system, because they do not understand the many different kinds of internal rules in

DNA, the algorithms by which genes are expressed. Biologists know the alphabet but not the grammar of the genes: they can describe the surface but not the principles which lie beneath the surface. Until these principles are known there will be neither a theory of biology nor a theory of evolution, in the full sense of the word. Biologists share with linguists a sense of frustration at the slow progress of their investigations".

One can sense, here, a cry of disillusion and despair in protest at the endless stream of superficial and unjustified conclusions which proceed from Dawkins and his unruly buccaneers, as they sail the shallow, murky waters of chance, under the largely discredited and tattered ensign of the truly infamous hypothesis of natural selection. The future, not only of biology but of all the sciences, lies in a unified theory of science. Scientists are fond of paying lip service to this proposal, but not a single step has been made in this direction.

We have seen that free will really does exist. Every new experience represents evolutionary progress, one more word in the book of life, and every life, one more line. Darwin was correct in saying that evolution is the vast accumulation of change but change is never continuous and not always small. All experiences come in quanta, in sets. Those who side with Gould are appalled at the way those who side with Dawkins elbow out culture; but the dogmatic ideas of the former on social and political structure, tend to destroy free will, in the sense of Big Brother. So we move from the pan of evolutionary psychology to the fire of an Orwellian nightmare where everyone (we trust) has free will but some are freer, and freer with their will, than others. Philosophy is fine but unless you introduce free will as a *scientific* concept, responsible for evolution, it remains no more than a chimera. Darwinists claim a long list of successes for their theory, we see only a long list of failures. Darwinism says that all kinds of chance mutation are possible and there is an enormous length of time to create evolution. But (A): Darwinism cannot produce a single favourable mutation; this in itself disproves the theory. (B): An enormous length of time? Really? Not when one considers the enormous size of the evolutionary construction. The theory requires that species stop mutating when they become well adapted, which is a large fraction of their existence. Considering that evolution only began in earnest with the Cambrian explosion, a mere 560 million years ago, how could the enormous organisation of mammalian existence have arisen in so short a time from chance alone. So Darwinists are split into those who believe in continuous or discontinuous evolution (punctuated equilibrium, "hopeful monsters"). Darwinists never talk to, only at (or about), each other because they are only capable of making logical premises, unsupported by a real deductive theory. (C): The theory cannot explain the origin of life. Life appeared as soon as conditions on earth were suitable, which totally eliminates the feasibility of chance, which would require an almost noncomputable period of time for life to originate. This discovery is the last nail in the coffin of natural selection. Dismayed by the difficulties of discovering the origin of life, molecular biologists gradually lost interest. The main reason for this is that supramacromolecules are present in all living systems, but there has been no success in making these in the laboratory. (D): There is no theory of prebiotic systems, no theory of ontogenetic development, no systems theory of any kind. (E): There is no definition of species, no theory of phylogeny and no discovery of new species, including the species which can talk and talk about evolution. A single remark is sufficient to emphasise the great disparity between the two theories: in Darwin's theory, human biological evolution ceased about a million years ago; but in our theory cultural and biological evolution are fused, cultural experience causing genetic mutations. So man's biocultural evolution progresses at the fast rate of his cultural evolution, which is now faster than it has ever been. Evolution - a slow process? The train of evolution travels faster and faster through the landscape of time with ever greater discontinuities in rate.

The Micro-Evolution of a Prebiotic System

There are two kinds of CPT violation in a prebiotic system: first, C,P,T violation and second, C or P (but not T) violation. The latter are reversible since they do not violate T. The latter, but not the former, were already present in non-living systems. In abiotic systems, the C or P (but not T) violating interactions, are exclusive to macromolecules and are always *causally* related. Amino acids in abiotic systems (not being macromolecules) are never created by this kind of interaction: they are formed by interactions, which violate CP and T (but not CPT). It is always C which is violated and never P. This is because the molecule and its mirror image always coexist, that is P is not violated. (When CP is violated, but not CPT, only C or P is violated). With this knowledge is it possible to discover if both amino acid and nucleotide were created by CPT violation in a prebiotic system? Since both molecules are handed, the interactions for both amino acid and nucleotide, violate P. This clarifies the issue considerably. Suppose nucleotide interactions are always reversible, which molecular biologists believe to be the case: then nucleotide interactions violate P and not T and so also not C, if they violate CPT. (If they violate C and P they do not violate CP and so, do not violate CPT). That is, they violate P and CPT.

The reasoning is no more difficult for protein. Since protein interaction is irreversible, amino acid interactions must also be assumed to be irreversible. So these interactions violate T. We have seen they violate P. So PT combined is not violated; therefore C is violated, if CPT is violated. So amino acid interaction in a prebiotic system violates C,P,T (that is, all, separately) and CPT. This is the mathematical solution we are seeking, but it is paradoxical, since it has been posited that molecules, formed from CPT violation, are macro or supramacro, whereas amino acid and nucleotide are not macro, yet are so formed. The reason for this is we have yet to take into account the role of acausality in living systems. It was explained before that this is important in systems which transfer information, structures of one type causing structures of another. Whereas, in abiotic systems, structures are always causal, in prebiotic and biotic systems they are both causal and acausal. To discover the meaning and significance of this, we must retrace our steps and make a more profound examination of the evolution of a prebiotic system.

The structure of nucleic acid is analogous to language structure: it is not the molecules themselves which matter, it is their ordering which conveys a message, whose information bears instructions for protein specificity. The invariant relations of language structure are acausal. It is then assumed that, in prebiotic systems, interactional structures are of two kinds: causal relations and acausal relations. Interactional structures which are abiotic are always causal, never acausal. Living systems behave like language systems: the meaning of the gene, like that of the word, does not lie in its nature but in its relation to other genes and to the universe. It is reasonable to assume that the molecular constituents, necessary to construct an amino acid, were present at the origin of a prebiotic system. It is now proven that these assumptions are sufficient to establish the origin and evolution of a prebiotic system.

A prebiotic system must, at its origin, be markedly different from any other open system, since it has the potential for the creation of life. This difference is that it has the two kinds of violation of CPT. In the abiotic world there is only one such violation, that which produces macromolecules. It cannot be assumed that macromolecules existed at the origin of a prebiotic system, since it can only be assumed that amino acid and nucleotide constituents exist at the origin, but not the amino acids or nucleotides themselves, and so, not macromolecular chains of amino acids or nucleotides.

The nonexistence of macromolecules, at this first stage, would seem to contradict the violation of CPT. Macromolecules (and, as we shall see, supramacromolecules also) can only come into existence when the structural relations are causal. We shall postulate that, at the origin of a prebiotic system, the structural relations are acausal. The system does not have encoding molecules but, from the outset, it develops the potential for an encoding system which, like any linguistic system, is formed from acausal relations. There is no invariant time ordering of the relations between the interactions of the constitutive molecules of amino acid or nucleotide. So the structural relations are acausal.

We must discover which of the two CPT violations is protein interaction and which is nucleotide interaction. Biochemists regard nucleic acid interactions as reversible in living systems; nucleotide interactions must also be so in prebiotic systems. In a living system it is clearly the much more interactive and much more important proteins that create the organisation of the system and not the more passive, phlegmatic nucleic acid. It is then the protein interactions which violate T and not the nucleic acids. In the prebiotic system it is the amino acid interactions which violate T and not the nucleotide interactions. Amino acid interactions violate C, P and T while nucleotide interactions violate P or C but not T. As already mentioned, at the origin of a prebiotic system nucleotide interactions and amino acid interactions violate P (the latter also violate C and T). This explains the handedness (sometimes called the chirality) of both amino acid and the sugar constituent of the nucleotide. It is easily seen that the molecules of living things must be handed. If this were not so a long molecular sequence would have a non-reproducible, almost infinitely varied, assortment of differently handed possibilities instead of a uniquely definable, easily reproducible, structure with a sharply specified function.

Now that we know which molecule has which asymmetric interaction—since this is a causally deterministic theory—the next step must be to find if we can establish a causal relation, in the prebiotic system, that involves these interactions. This possibility is suggested by the encoding of primary protein structure by nucleic acid. These molecules are not aloof but intimately related and causally dependent. Since causality has been defined, it cannot be assumed that this causal relation, should it exist, points from nucleotide to amino acid. The so-called dogma of one-way communication of information has in any case proved false. We must keep an open mind. Let us examine the logical consequences of the theory, without prejudice and without succumbing to the seductive lure of glib expounders of the Darwinian roulette wheel. Chance is no more the dominant concept of biology than it is for physics.

Nucleotides do not exist prior to the existence of a prebiotic system, but amino acids do. With our emphasis on the primacy of the concept of real progressive evolution, it is logical to assume that the asymmetric interactions, which produce amino acids, must have evolved such as to cause, at the origin of a prebiotic system, the formation of the first nucleotides. We have already seen that this system is not like any other open system but must be assumed to have the potentiality for encoding (realised in the living system). This will be so if it is postulated that, instead of interactions of one kind of violation causing interactions of the other kind, we postulate that molecules, constructed by interactions of one kind of violation, cause molecules constructed by interactions of the other kind of violation. This is the first time, in the process of evolution, that molecules have caused molecules. Till then, only interactions between molecules caused interactions between molecules. Before, interactions between things caused interactions between things; now things cause things. This postulate is suggested by the fact that a DNA molecule encodes primary protein structure. As yet, we have no actual encoding, nor even a polypeptide structure, but we do have the potential for this.

It is now possible to state the first step in the evolution of a prebiotic system.

This law states that the origin of a prebiotic system occurs when a set of invariant (under GCT) relations between acausally related CPT violating interactions of the constitutive molecules of an amino acid, causes a set of invariant relations between acausally related CPT violating interactions of the constitutive molecules (phosphate, pentose, base) of a nucleotide. (The CPT violation in the first case is C, P, T and in the second, P.). The meaning of the law is that a prebiotic system is one with two kinds of CPT violating interactions, between simple molecules, which construct amino acid and nucleotide. The first step in its evolution occurs when an amino acid molecule causes the formation of a nucleotide molecule, that is, the structure of the former causes the structure of the latter. (The structure identifies the molecule.) This means that at a time when information could not pass in the direction from nucleotide to amino acid it did pass in the reverse direction. This contradicts Darwin's theory, which denies such a possibilty.

It was seen that when a prebiotic system becomes biotic we must allow the possibility not only of *invariant* time-ordered relations between causally related supra-molecular interactions, but also the possibility of *non-invariant* time-order relations between causally related interactions. This is because in the prebiotic system there only exist non-invariant time-ordered relations. This allows choice to enter quantum mechanics, in the selection of non-invariant time-order relations which, we have seen, is potentially creative in character. Because biotic systems behave like language systems, we must allow the inverse of this: that is, not only the existence of *non-invariant* time-ordered relations between acausally related interactions but the formation also of invariant time-ordered relations between acausally related supra-molecular interactions (replace invariant by non-invariant and vice versa; also replace causal with acausal). The relations between the symbols of a language are obviously not causal since they can be chosen purely arbitrarily, but they cannot be associated with a meaning unless they have an invariant time order relation. Biotic systems break free from the harness of causality to become creative and, inversely, create a harness of causality to memorise their creativity and control and direct its expression.

The two most important interactions between molecules in living systems are the covalent bond and the hydrogen bond. These are the only kinds of interaction we need be concerned with. In nucleic acids, the covalent bonding is spatial and the hydrogen bond is a charge bond. The latter bond must have evolved after the spatial bond, since the limbs of helical nucleic acid cannot relate until they have been formed in the first place and the nucleotides are linked by spatial bonding. We have seen that the molecular interactions which constitute an amino acid are not causally related since there is no invariant time-ordering between the molecular interactions. This contrasts with the formation of invariant time-ordered polypeptide chains of amino acids. So evolution of the prebiotic system began with the formation of a set of invariant spatial relations between *non*-causally related molecular interactions which violate C, P and T. This set, which is an amino acid structure—the basic unit of protein structure—causes a set of invariant spatial relations between a set of *non*-causally related molecular interactions which violate P. The latter interactions are the covalently bonded sugar, base and phosphate molecules which together constitute a nucleotide. These nucleotide bonds are formed with no invariant time-ordering, so there is an acausal relation between the molecular interactions as is the case with the formation of amino acids just mentioned.

In the next step, initiated as always by the protein interactions (the driving interactions), a set of invariant spatial relations is formed between *causally* related amino-acid interactions which violate C, P and T. The relation is *causal* because amino acids only string together like a well strung necklace with the beads in a specific invariant (under GCT) logical time-ordered molecular ordering. The spatial ordering, being logically causal, cannot be reversed; each amino acid cannot cheat but must join the queue. (The ordering is from the N end to the CO end of the polypeptide chain.) This spatialordering is also a causal time-ordering. By an earlier law, the formation of a macro-molecule requires that there be the formation of a set of invariant charge or spatial relations between *causally* related interactions which violate CPT. This string of amino acids is the first *macro*-molecule to be formed in a prebiotic system. It may be defined as a macroprotein. It is still to evolve into a supramacro-protein. As just described, this set causes a set of invariant spatial relations between *causally* related nucleotide interactions, which violate P and, of course, CPT. This string of nucleotides (a polynucleotide) is likewise a *macro*-molecule. It may be defined as a macro-nucleic acid. It is still to evolve into a supramacro-nucleic acid. The nucleotides are *causally* related, because they must conform to a logical invariant (under GCT) time-ordered molecular ordering, from the 5′ to the 3′ end of the chain. The formation of a C violating hydrogen bond interaction, all-important in the construction of protein and nucleic acid, must now enter the process. The hydrogen bond is always a causal interaction because of complementary pairing of bases.

Beginning again with the evolving protein, the formation of a set of invariant charge relations between *causally* related interactions which violate C, P and T, causes the formation of a set of invariant charge relations, between *causally* related interactions, which violate P, namely the covalently bonded P violating interactions between nucleotide sugar and base. The relations are causal, because they are logically complementary base pairings. These relations have produced a ladder formation. The addition of this set of structural relations to either molecule, even though it is causal, does not produce a supramacro, since this formation obeys only the macrostructural law. So how does such a molecule evolve? So far we have had only invariant charge *or* spatial relations between causally related interactions: analogously, the condition for the formation of supramacro must be the formation of *both* invariant spatial *and* charge relations between *causally* related interactions. The next evolutionary step is the prelude but cannot, however, produce supramacro. There are two possibilities: first, the distance between the steps of the ladder was fixed, followed by the distance between the limbs of the ladder being fixed, or second, the same process in reverse order. The C-violating H-bond interactions between base pairs in the evolving nucleic acid molecule are non-causally related, because there is no interaction between the bases of different pairings. If there were, the coding system would not work. It follows that invariant charge and spatial *non*-causal relations must be formed before invariant charge and spatial *causal* relations. Therefore, in the next evolutionary step, the formation of a set of invariant spatial and charge relations, between *non*-causally related protein interactions, which violate C, P, T, causes the formation of a set of invariant spatial and charge relations, between *non*-causally related nucleic acid interactions, which violate C, the H-bond interactions between base pairs. Because the relations between interactions are non-causal, the molecules are still not supramacro. The hydrogen bonds are, as a result, stacked at a precise distance from one another (the ladder steps), but the distance between the side chains is still not precise. Only one final step is needed to make this distance precise and complete the structure of the supramacro protein and nucleic acid.

The formation of a set of invariant spatial and charge relations between *causally* related supramacro-protein interactions, which violate C, P and T, causes the formation of a set of invariant spatial and charge relations between causally related supramacro-nucleic acid interactions which violate P, namely the covalently bonded P violating interactions between sugar and base of the nucleotide. The nucleic acid so formed is a molecule of DNA. It assumes a helical formation. Both molecules are supramacro as they obey the required law. The widely held RNA hypothesis is disproved; life did not begin with RNA but with the co-evolution of protein and DNA. DNA has two chains and must have two because it is a supra, which cannot be formed unless there is a preceding stage of C-violation, producing a two-chain ladder. Life could not have begun with RNA, since it is only a one-chain molecule and not supramacro, (it is about 80 bases long.) We have created supramacro nucleic acid and protein with charge and spatial structure. Sometimes the interactions are causally related, sometimes they are not. By symmetry of C, P, T violation, there must also be a temporal structure. This temporal structure must be preceded by both a spatial and a charge structure so that it can only exist for supramacromolecules. Molecules do not have a time structure: so we postulate a new kind of thing, an experience of feeling, which does have, and only has, a time structure. Feelings are created by the life of the organism by its process of selection. A life is a set of experiences. As this is a quantum theory, it is impossible to say, in principle, precisely when this life begins. Not even god, so to speak, knows the precise instant of creation.

When life begins, the entropy of the macrosystem increases, unilaterally, at some unpredictable instant. This is the law of the macroscopic origin of life. When life is created in the laboratory, as it inevitably will, it will take everyone by surprise. It is assumed that experiences exist only in time (and not in space), since they only have a time structure. They are a new kind of organisation, because an organisation is identified by its structure and this structure is new. Since they are a new kind of thing, formed by organizing molecular interactions, they must, by analogy with abiotic structures, be assumed to be at a higher level of organisation than molecules. They are constructed of life by analogy with particles being constructed of energy. Before invariant time-ordered relations exist there only exist non-invariant time-ordered relations. An experience of feeling organises supra-molecular interactions, since the life of the biotic system selects non-invariant time-ordered relations between them, for the purpose of creating its structure, defined as its consciousness, which is a set of invariant (under GCT) time-ordered relations between supramacro interactions which violate CPT. This directed, creative agency of selection is responsible for the enormous concentration of organisation even in micro-organisms, which it achieves by violating the logical laws of causality which are valid in non-living systems. The consciousness of the experience is, clearly, a set of functional relations of the organism. The consciousness of the cell relates the life of the cell to its external environment which supplies the energy and materials (food) necessary for its evolutionary development. A life, which is a set of experiences, in selecting an experience, is selecting a molecularly defined function of the organism. In causally relating experiences, it is causally relating functions and is therefore creating the metabolic organismic functionality.

It was seen that the macroscopic origin of life is the unilateral increase of entropy and life of a biotic system. Analogous to there being a microscopic explanation of the second law of thermodynamics, there is a microscopic explanation of these macroscopic laws. Function can only be explained microscopically. A living system has function, because it has a life which selects in the performance of function. A computer is not creative, its function exists only in the mind which creates it. Brian Goodwin has said that you have to look for creativity from within the organism. There does exist a creator, not an external creator in the Paley sense: it is the life of the organism. Creation comes from within or not at all - an organism dies when it ceases to be a creator (it may lose the will to create). Computers, like old soldiers, never die, they only fade away!

This question of function produces the most difficult logical problem of all in the science of life. One which has blocked all progress in this field and made it seem an impenetrable mystery. Bohr declared the analogous problem of mind to be insoluble, as did the philosopher Colin McGinn. The problem is one of circularity. A life is a set of experiences: so, no experiences, no life. But for experiences to exist, since they are structured, a life must select non-invariant relations between molecular interactions: so, no life, no experiences. At the beginning of the last century, Einstein pointed the way. He was faced with a problem of circularity: to synchronize clocks you need a synchronizing signal of known velocity, but how can a signal velocity be known if there are no synchronized clocks with which to measure it? Einstein's breathtaking solution was to break into the circle and assert the signal velocity of light to be a constant, c, note well, an absolute. Since momentous consequences followed from this, one must expect likewise, if one follows Einstein's example and enters the circle of this biological paradox. We met this circularity again in ontological logic: to define truth you have to do so in terms of some known reality. But how can the definition of reality be known to be true without a prior definition of truth? The circle is entered by asserting a definition of absolute reality to be true, a priori, as a law of logic, which is a law of universal logic because it relates to the universe; then we define truth in terms of this reality in whose truth we have faith, thereby unifying religion with science.

We enter the present circle by asserting that the existence of a life comes before the existence of its parts. A life at its origin has no experiences: the whole comes before the parts! The real biophysical thing, a life, is a truly spiritual entity because the whole exists even when the parts do not. The set of elements exists before its elements. Life begins as an empty set. Only a quantum theory of the universe could produce and resolve so astounding a paradox. But, in mathematical language, we find things no less strange: in infinite set theory a part may be as large as the whole, now we have a whole—which is a real thing by a former law of logic—

coming into existence before any of its parts. This is impossible for things, which exist in space but these things exist only in time. It can be seen from this why the time dimension seems so incomprehensible: it is because its logic appears to be contradictory. The seemingly insoluble paradox is resolved if it is assumed that life begins as an empty set. Mathematics is the language of science. Set theory is the predominant theory of mathematics. Imaginary numbers were found to be indispensable to physical science, which made them respectable. The null (empty) set, though indispensable to set theory, has received no sanction of respectability from universal science, itself a valuable clue to the next step in the evolution of science. This is amended by employing the null set to resolve the paradox. A prebiotic system evolves into a biotic system when it creates a life, which is a null set. (Think of a list (set) of your favourite films, or a list of all the things you have to take on holiday, at first an empty set. It is worth remarking that if one of the items on the list is the list itself the list is a self-membered set, which means we need a new set theory.) A life, even when a null set, is real (it symbolises reality). It selects non-invariant relations between interactions with the purpose of creating experiences. But what kind of relations and between what interactions? The answer to this question is the solution to the problem of the origin of function and so to the microscopic origin of life.

17

FUNCTIONALITY

Analogous to real structures existing in space-time, we must now construct real structures which exist only in time, that is, experiential structures. Since DNA cannot be transcribed until encoding is first produced, it is assumed that a life, which is an empty set, selects non-invariant time-ordered *non*-causal relations between supramacro-protein interactions which violate C, P and T, with the purpose of creating a set of invariant time-ordered, non-causal relations between supramacro-protein interactions which violate C, P and T. It is only in a biotic system that invariant time-ordered relations exist between noncausally related interactions. (This is inversely analogous to the existence, solely in biotic systems, of non-invariant time-ordered relations between causally related interactions.). This produces an experience, which is a set of invariant time-ordered *non*-causal relations between protein interactions, which violate CPT. This causes an experience which is a set of invariant time-ordered *non*-causal relations between supramacro-DNA base-pair (H-bonded) interactions which violate C.

Base-pair interactions causally relate P violating interactions (between sugar and base), but are never themselves causally related. Any invariant time-ordering they acquire is entirely a result of the selective creativity of the life of the cell. This invariant time-ordering is not dependent on their having a causal relation, for there is none. This caused experience, which is a functional set of invariant time-ordered acausal relations, is a favourable biological mutation. A favourable mutation is always a set, never a point mutation, which may be neutral or harmful. Evolution is never continuous, it always proceeds in jumps, in sets. Some jumps are bigger than others. The mutation is favourable because, being an experience, it always adds entropy to the body and life to the life of the organism. A gene is defined as the *set* of bases which is organised by a mutation. Only this set (the set as a whole) encodes primary protein structure. A mutation is a new experience, a set of invariant time-ordered relations, which organises a set of (acausally related) DNA base-pair interactions. This new experience is caused by a new experience which is a set of invariant time-ordered relations, which organises a set of (acausally related) protein interactions. Ontogenetic evolution is always progressive and can only be advanced by lived experience. Our theory explains the development of the organism, Darwin's has nothing to say about ontogeny. There is no royal road, no shortcut, cloning or otherwise, to a more evolutionary advanced organism or species. In the language of religion, god has ordained it so: you only get something out if you put something in; you don't get nowt for nowt. There is justice in nature in this sense. Living requires effort and effort is ultimately rewarded in the life of the species. Evolution doesn't come free. But where is the raw material for the exercise of free will—the selection of non-invariant time-ordered relations between base-pairs—to come from?

Introns

Evolutionary phylogenetic progress brings increasing diversification: the more advanced the organism, the more capacity for non-invariant selection there is, that is the greater the exercise of free will by the organism. In bacteria you'd expect to have great difficulty in finding any free will:

though it exists in all organisms, it is almost non-existent in bacteria. But in ascending the progressive evolutionary ladder one would expect the exercise of free will, and the resultant diversity of choice associated with this, to be increasingly evident. The less automatic the behaviour the greater the free-will, but not even a bacterium is a robot. Introns, the nonencoding bases of the genome are almost, but not entirely, nonexistent in bacteria but increasingly prevalent in higher animals. They are a maximum in humans, being over ninety per cent of the genome. They are referred to as "junk" DNA. The idea of all these bases being useless is absurd, considering the immensity of organisation and fine-ordering of an organism. You might just as well expect the traffic at peak hour on Oxford Street to operate effectively if the entire area was strewn with large obstructions. Introns are the very substance, the source of creativity; they are essential to the living process, being used for the purpose of the formation of non-invariant time-ordered selections. These are nonencoding but their non-invariant time-ordered selection, based on the ever-increasing learning of the life of the organism, succeeds in producing a mutation, a set of invariant time-ordered acausal relations between base-pairs, which encodes the formation of new protein needed for the progressive development of the organism.

Introns are not static, they jump about on the genome. This supports the theory, since the process of selection causes this to happen. Barbara McLintock discovered the existence of jumping genes in experiments on maize. In 1978 Walter Gilbert of Howard University, suggested that introns could speed up evolution by promoting genetic recombination between exons. This process (which he called "exon shuffling") would be directly associated with the foundation of new genes. Introns, from this perspective, have a profound purpose. They serve as hotspots for recombination in the formation of new combinations of exons. They are in our genes because they have been used during evolution as a pathway to assemble new genes. The exon shuffling idea has been supported by data from various experimental approaches. This strongly supports the idea of the present theory that the role of introns is profound and a selection of non-invariant relations between introns is being made, with the purpose of creating invariant encoding relations.

The formation of time-ordered acausal relations has been described. Mutations consist solely of acausal, never of causal, relations. Having formed these acausal relations to produce mutations, the life of the organism selects non-invariant time-ordered *causal* relations between supramacro-protein interactions, which violate C, P and T. This produces a new experience, which is a set of invariant time-ordered *causal* relations between supramacro-protein interactions which violate C, P and T. This causes the life to select non-invariant time-ordered causal relations between base-sugar supramacro DNA interactions which violate P, to produce a new experience, which is a set of invariant time-ordered *causal* relations between base-sugar supramacro DNA interactions, which violate P. The latter set of invariant time-order causal relations transcribe the DNA code. Experiences at the protein level cause the encoding structure of DNA and cause the processes of transcription and translation, which DNA encodes. The primary protein structure which results is the outcome of the choice of experiences made by the life in its developmental process.

Transcription, Translation and Replication

The processes of transcription, translation and replication proceed, in principle, in the way just described, by the formation of experiences with a causal structure. First, the meaning of the transcription process is explained.

The time ordering of the base pairs, acausally related in a mutation is no less fixed than the spatial and charge relations (let's drop our prejudice about the reality of time relations - time is here to stay!). Suppose we focus our attention on a particular base-pair, A-T say, which must immediately precede say, the pair G-C. Although this time-ordering is fixed for these acausally related base-pair interactions until there is a fixed time-ordering for *causal* relations, the H-bond causal relation A-T could be T-A and the causal relation G-C could be C-G. In a non-living system there is no *choice* since a causal relation, in which particle transfer occurs, must have an invariant time-order relation. But the life of the organism can freely select the time order, A-T or T-A, testing, non-invariantly, the proteins which result from these pairings, in functional protein interaction: the choice which maximizes the life of the organism is the invariant time-ordered causal relation, which is an invariant relation in the set of a new experience, as described in the previous section. The life of the organism does not have to know this any more than an isolated system has to know of its unilaterally increasing entropy. The causal relation is the result of base complementarity. If A is chosen first it necessarily produces T; if T is chosen first it necessarily produces A; a causal relation exists, whatever the time order relation. That is why choice (free will) can exist. It does so because there is something to be selected. In the non-living world there is nothing which can be selected. Free will liberates nature from the tyranny of time order invariance associated with causality, to produce non-invariant time-ordered causal relations. It also, inversely, liberates nature from the tyranny of time-order noninvariance associated with acausality, in the case of base-pair interactions, to produce invariant time-ordered acausal relations. If we imagine the DNA ladder to stand upright, the shuffling of the genetic cards happens in two ways: in a vertical direction, acausally, and in a horizontal direction, causally. The life of the organism, in its process of selection, flits up and down, and from side to side, along the ladder in a perpetual quest to better its life. There is no hint here of the Darwinist emphasis on numbers: reproduction is all. It is the quality of life which matters. It is no paradox that the quality of life is defined quantitatively. The more life a life creates the better it is. Which is the best bank? The one that gives you the most money. We have no need of a Maxwell demon here: the "demon" is the life of the organism, which does not exist in the body of the organism, since it only exists in time, but it does control time-order relations between bodily interactions. We must drop our prejudice against time: time is real, life is real, experiences are real, you, that is, your life (believe it or not!) is real; but you only exist in time, it's your body which exists in space. (You are the invisible man! but don't worry - your secret is safe with me.) We are such real stuff as spirits are made of and (with apologies to the Bard), our little life is rounded with a mathematical set.

Replication

Replication is causally ordered, as it always proceeds with a specific time-ordering, from the 5' end to the 3' end of the DNA template strand. During replication, the organism creates mutations by the non-causal method already described. These are transcribed and translated by the causal process just mentioned. The non-invariant selections of the non-causal process are tried out in conjunction with the feedback of the causal process. The feedback, which is selected, is that which, on trial, produces the most viable protein. The process of life is a ceaselessly creative juggling of non-invariant time-ordered relations to optimize the consciousness of the organism. The purpose is not merely to survive: it is to create the best possible life, to maximize the consciousness of the organism, which means to create as much life as possible. Every organism aims for the stars (and in human life every human wants to be a star!) This certainly contradicts the Darwinist conception that survival is all. After the primary protein structure is formed, the higher hierarchical levels of protein structure are formed by self-organisation—as described for prebiotic systems—to produce the overall molecular shape. The rate of formation is much higher in biotic systems since the entropy increases unilaterally. Without this rapid self-organisation an organism could not respond quickly enough to a changing environment, nor perform its complex metabolic functions at sufficient speed for its survival and development. The two chains of DNA are antiparallel, which means that the phosphate diesters between major deoxyribose units, read 3' to 5' on one chain and 5' to 3' on the other. On replication, an A on the parent strand causes a T to appear on the daughter strand, and not the reverse (that is a daughter T does not cause a parent A); likewise, a T on the parent strand causes an A on the daughter strand (and not the reverse). By the learning process of non-invariant selection, the life must discover the correct time order of bases, which produces maximization.

An experience of feeling, created at the protein level, causes an experience of feeling (and so a mutation) at the DNA level. But causation is not symmetrical. An experience of feeling, at the DNA level, only causes the creation of protein structure (feedback), not the causation of a feeling at the protein level. The latter feeling is uncaused. Life is, primarily, a top-down process. See Table 6.

Table 6
Prebiotic and Biotic System

ORGANISATION	SYMMETRY VIOLATION	STRUCTURE OF ORGANISATION
1. macromolecule of an abiotic system	CPT; C or P	a set of invariant charge *or* spatial relations between *causally* related molecular interactions which violate C or P. Reversible interactions.
2. DNA precursor nucleotide molecule of a prebiotic system. Not a macromolecule	CPT; P	a set of invariant spatial relations between acausally related sugar, base and phosphate interactions which violate P. Reversible interactions.
3. DNA MACROMOLECULAR single linear nucleotide strand (composed of nucleotides)	CPT; P	a set of invariant spatial relations between *causally* related nucleotide interactions which violate P. Strand forms in a single direction only.
4. DNA nonencoding double-stranded linear nucleotide macromolecule with no fixed step or ladder distance.	CPT; P	a set of invariant charge relations between *causally* related sugar-base nucleotide interactions which violate P. Strands form in opposite directions
5. DNA nonencoding double-stranded linear macromolecular nucleotide with invariant step distance and non-invariant strand distance	CPT; C violated for base-pair interactions	a set of invariant charge *and* spatial relations between *acausally* related complimentary base-pair macromolecular interactions which violate C
6. DNA encoding double stranded supramacromolecule with invariant step and invariant strand distance	CPT; P	a set of invariant charge *and* spatial relations between *causally* related sugar-base *supramacromolecular* interactions which violate P.

7. An experience of feeling which is a mutation of encoding DNA; encodes primary protein structure.	CPT; C	a set of invariant time- ordered relations between *acausally* related c-violating base-pair *supramacromolecular* interaction. The life of the system selects non invariant time ordered relations to create the set.
8. An experience of feeling which is the fed-back protein (amino acid) expression of encoding DNA by transcription and translation.	CPT; P	a set of invariant time ordered relations between *causally* related P violating sugar-base *supramacromolecular* interactions which causes primary protein structure. The life of the system selects non invariant time ordered relations to create the set.

NOTE: the invariance in the table is invariance under GCT

18

THE MEASURE OF
LIFE OF AN ORGANISM

The consciousness of an experience is the measure of its life, the thing (analogous to energy) which the experience organises; the measure of the thing, life, is also a measure of its organisation (the number of its structural relations). The measure of thing and the measure of organisation are fused, identical, for life, but not for non-living things (mass and entropy). The larger the consciousness of an experience, the larger its magnitude, the more functionally related it is to the universe. A large experience causes a larger mutation than a smaller experience, which means a larger progressive change in ontology. Mutations are quantitatively graded. They are also qualitatively graded since the higher the level of the experience, the larger the mutation they are able to cause. For about half the evolution of life on earth organisms were single-celled, then multi-cellular animals evolved. The life of the latter (eukaryotes) is constructed by the lives of the organismic sub-cells, which co-operate to create the holistic life of the organism. Each cell has an autonomous life, which co-operates by a process of interaction with other cell lives. Each life, at whatever hierarchical level, can select each of its experiences independently. Analogous to the law of entropy summation for independent systems we have: the life of a biotic system is the sum of the lives of its experiences. The life of an organism is more, usually much more, than the sum of the lives of its cells; the whole is more than the sum of its parts. The reason individuals co-operate is that, by creating a life much larger than themselves, with a greater relation to the universe, they procure for themselves a greater life than they would if independent; (it's better to be a small fish in a large pool than the reverse). The law of maximization necessitates co-operation. The nature and degree of the co-operation is part of the learning process. The games theory of Darwinism is a constructive approach to this process. It's not only organisms which are social creatures, the cells of an organism are also. An organism is a social creature at two different hierarchical levels. A new experience in the life of an organism causes a (favourable) heritable mutation in the hereditary DNA. A new experience in the life of a cell, tissue or organ of an organism causes a mutation only in somatic DNA (which is not heritable). A cell which does not co-operate in the life of an organism, plays no functional role and dies. To function is to relate; to relate is to co-operate in the creation of a life at a higher level of organisation. The individuality of an organism can only be expressed through co-operation. Different somatic structures have different DNA because their experiences, which cause mutation in DNA, are different, that is, their time-ordered functionality is different. Different organisms have different DNA. The more different their experiences, the more different their DNA. Man's DNA is more different than any other species and is becoming more so at an ever-faster rate. We are time blind. The more we understand the all-important invariant time ordering structure of DNA, the more different from one another will the DNA of different organisms appear and the more will we appreciate the vast gulf which separates the order of magnitude of the molecular organisation of humans from that of all other animals.

19

PHYLOGENETIC EVOLUTION

Experiences exist at different levels of organisation, creating different levels of relationship with the universe and with reality. A relation created at one level implies the relations created at lower levels. Feelings, sensory experience and cognition are, clearly, vastly different in their mode of consciousness. With the experience of touching, an organism can establish that there exists something which is not itself but it cannot do this with feeling. With the experience of seeing, an organism can establish the existence of a world independent of itself, but it cannot do this with feeling or touching. With the experience of cognition, an organism can establish a symbolic relationship between the world and experience, but it cannot do this with sensory experience or with feelings. You cannot see an experience, but you can know an experience. This means that there has been a progressive evolution of experience to ever higher levels of consciousness. A life is defined as a set of experiences. A mind is a subset of a life, being analogously defined as a set of cognitive experiences (experiences of knowing). Do the lives, which possess experiences, also exist at different levels of organisation?

Organisms communicate both vocally and by body language, using symbols and signs (man also uses concepts in speech). This means their experiences and lives interact. So there is logical ground, analogously, for assuming that, just as the plurality of lives of cells interact to create the single life of an an organism, so the lives of organisms interact to form a higher life, the life of a species. A life at any level of organisation is defined as the set of all its experiences. The lowest level of organisation of life is the life of a cell, since only a macrosystem can possess a life, a molecule cannot. Analytical reductionists suffer from the delusion that molecules are alive. Stuart Kauffman, for example, who believes in a systems approach, does not. The lives of the cells of an organism interact, because the cell functions must relate to create the life and, therefore, the development as a whole. This easily explains the otherwise puzzling existence of sexual reproduction. Analogously, organisms must interact not only experientially, but bodily, to create the life of the species. This one life has many bodies, each with a separate spatial existence, but since they all interact, they collectively form a single, spatially differentiated body. The life of the species has, in this sense, conquered space. It has been left to the life of man, alone, to conquer time.

The life of an organism is not the set of the experiences of its cells, because it may contain experiences at a higher level than the experiences of its cells; for example, cells do not see or know. This is not so at the higher level of the life of a species, which opens up new possibilities. The life of species is defined as the evolving set of all the experiences of the organisms which create it. The life of a species, like the life of an organism, is an evolving set, new experiences being born and past experiences, which are no longer useful, being eliminated. A new experience in the life of a species, having been created by ontogeny is both a new ontogenetic and phylogenetic experience and causes a hereditary mutation, as do new ontogenetic experiences. Phylogenetic change is not produced by Darwinian chance but is solely a consequence of directed mutation caused by new experience. Perhaps the most convincing experimental evidence for the existence of a species life is the behaviour of honeybees in seeking a new site for a nest. A swarm behaves, as with a single life, on the basis of the dances of individual bees which have scouted the possibilities. These bees communicate with body language, highly effective in the manufacture of honey, but no single bee decides the issue, only the swarm as a whole. Man possesses culture: religion, art and science, all dependent on the knowledge of law, which makes it increasingly evident that the genus Homo is evolving lives of species at progressively higher levels of consciousness. Each of these levels defines a new species of man. Man always progresses. Man is currently being described by authors as a supraorganism, with the internet being analogous to a brain. The great archaeologist-philosopher Pierre Teilhard pioneered this line of thought only to be dismissed as a dreamer, but books have been written since, by scientists, echoing his thought and attempting to give it a firm biological foundation.

Analogously, whenever the life of any species creates a new level of consciousness it creates a new species, defined by that new level of consciousness. Though Darwin's book is called *On the Origin of Species*, it has nothing to say about the origin of species. Darwinists have suggested that species originate by geographic isolation of populations. That the different kinds of variations produced in different populations sometimes produce a new species. The isolation of populations is more likely to hinder than promote the formation of new species since it reduces the possibilities of interaction between organisms. A new species is produced, discontinuously, when an individual of a species creates a discontinuity in consciousness, which is new in the life of the species, that is, discontinuous phylogenetic change. The same change could be produced by several populations of the same species, but it is always a single individual which is responsible for phylogenetic change. This is the true meaning of individuality, not the bogus Darwinian notion. The life of the species is ultimately determined by the lives of the individual members of the species.

Organisms must co-operate to create the life of the species. This co-operation sometimes conflicts with the law-governed necessity of the organism to maximize its life. Beware of false interpretations of the maximization law. There is no necessary relation between maximization and longevity; a short fruitful life is superior to a long fruitless one. Darwinists' considerable interest in Games theory is a departure from their own theory, since it has nothing to do with survival alone, implicit though this is, but asks instead: How shall the participants in a given life situation choose, such as to bring them maximum reward, or produce, at worst, a reasonable compromise? They are coming round to the present theory. The choice they make is the one which they judge will maximize their life, given the need to compromise, due to lack of information about the other parties. Quality, not just quantity, is the issue. Quality of life is created by cooperation. Cheats can reap the benefits without making a contribution, which endangers cooperation, so society must have laws punishing cheats. But natural selection only selects the individual who is in harsh competition with the rest of society. Darwinists, of all persuasions, are fascinated by Games theory and its implications. Brian Goodwin, anti-Darwinist, says it is co-operation which is primary and competition secondary. This conflict of choice, the necessity to choose in favour of the individual, at the expense of the species, is the scientific meaning of "original sin". Before man, the maximization law for the life of the organism has always been in conflict with the law which states that the lives of organisms create the life of the species. Competition has always vied with co-operation. Both have, thus far, always been present. Competition, alone, can only lead to extinction. (Rich countries, for their own safety and benefit, must always assist poorer countries, as we should now realise. Philanthropy is now the only enlightened self-interest.) In Darwin's theory, competition *alone* is what produces evolutionary fitness. Frequently, the relation between the life of the individual and the life of

171

the species is neutral or opposed. In Darwin's theory, altruism is just genetic selfishness since it occurs towards those with related genes. Utter nonsense. It is disproved by the following examples:

Throughout the animal kingdom there are innumerable examples of animals that risk their lives for the survival of the offspring and to protect other members of the group; in the human species altruism is still more apparent: the man who jumps into a swollen river to rescue a child he has never seen before; a climber who rescues a climber he will never see again; the flier who remains in his plane rather than parachute to safety to save the population below; the woman who makes sure everyone has left a collapsing building before leaving herself; and so on. Darwin recognised that his hypothesis cannot clear the major hurdle of altruism; our theory does so with no difficulty. The destinies of individual and species are linked. The species life moulds the destiny of the individual "rough-hew it how we will" (Shakespeare). The life of the individual is a marriage of contingency and necessity. As the evolution of man progresses, competition becomes increasingly less important than co-operation. The behaviour of a human who maximizes his life becomes increasingly likely, with the ever-increasingly complex societal relations of man's progressive evolution, to be favourable also to the evolution of the life of man. Man is in the process of creating a new species in which the interests of the individual and the species necessarily coincide. The human mind will then rise to a new level of consciousness in which it consciously creates the scientifically defined life of man as a predictably deterministic evolving life. ("To drift is to be in hell; to steer is to be in heaven" G. B. Shaw). The concept of man as a supraorganism evolving into yet another new species, is rapidly developing in the human mind. The first few million years of man's meteoric evolution is but the relatively insignificant prelude to the infinite ladder of progressive evolution of the emergent self-conscious mind of man, rising by discontinuous steps of ever-increasing magnitude. To prove this requires a revolution in mathematical set theory analogous to that of nonlinear geometry, with the formation of a new set of axioms for set theory (including self-membered sets).

Although the roots of modern experimental science go back only four hundred years, to Galileo, the roots of modern science go as far back as three and a half thousand years, to Moses. This is hidden from us because, in those days, the logic of universal science was fused with art in the form of the telling of stories, since this was the only way it could be communicated. Analogously, mysticism and philosophy were fused until the time of Socrates. Even Newton did not separate the practice of alchemy from real science. Christ fused the universal logic of moral science, consisting of nonmathematical laws, with stories, in the form of parables. Moses, a millennium earlier, constructed two sets of universal logical laws, one consisting of morals and the other of mathematical logical laws of the universe. He fused the latter, but not the former, with a story. The Eden myth, which owes its lasting fame to the mathematical logical laws of the universe which it expresses so poetically. The most important of these is the image law obeyed by the relation between reality and the life of man, which he states as a relation between god and man. Western civilization has failed to understand the significance of there being two trees in the Garden of Eden, not just a tree of knowledge, but a tree of life. The tree of life represents the evolving life of man, which is protected by cherubs, with a flaming sword. This means that the path of evolution, which creates the life of man, is strewn with the tortured and the dead, including Christ, who have aspired to create the life of man. It is a story of the cultural and therefore the biological evolution of man. It is a prophecy that the human mind will, one day, create the life of man with a discontinuity in consciousness and therefore, create a new species. The knowledge of morality created a discontinuity in consciousness.

(The human mind of the new species, Homo sapiens, defined by this discontinuity, was wise enough to realize it was naked of knowledge.) Before this, man lived in a fool's paradise of ignorance of morality. Paradise regained, not a fool's paradise, will come with knowledge of the tree of life, the life of man. To enable him to do this, sapiens developed a new feeling, that of conscience, which, with the discovery of mathematics a mere ten thousand years ago, enabled him to construct civilization. The goal was, at last, in sight. In the twentieth century, belief in a deterministic reality, in the existence of absolute truth and in the worth of conscience, strongly nurtured in the nineteenth century, have been largely eroded by scientists, including psychologists and psychiatrists. If this corrosive doubt, fostered and nourished by almost every form of media and by scientists themselves, is not to destroy civilization, scientists must reassert the true beliefs and values of human nature and a belief in the existence of an evolving human nature which Darwinism, in its folly, denies.

Even if chance mutations were favourable (they never are), there are not nearly enough of them in Darwin's theory to build the enormous edifice of evolution. There just aren't enough bricks. A mutation is generally held to occur about once every million years. The maverick Darwinist, Stephen Gould says that, with punctuated equilibrium, it is more like once every ten thousand years. This is still not nearly enough. It was seen that every new cultural experience in the life of man causes a phylogenetic mutation and that every new experience, of any kind, in the life of a species, causes a phylogenetic mutation. While it is true that man mutates more rapidly than other species, we can nevertheless get a good idea of the scale of change from man's evolution. To this end, we conservatively ignore the wealth of evolutionary change caused by his noncultural experience and ask how much mutation is caused by culture alone. At infants' school a child learns to speak, to acquire a vocabulary, a syntax and a grammar. He or she learns to understand stories, to sing, to compare volumes in vessels, to build model houses, to construct jigsaws and so on. This involves at least hundreds of experiences. At junior and senior school, a pupil learns mathematics, native and foreign languages, history, art, science. The number of experiences involved is in the thousands. Each new experience was discovered by an individual during the 3 million years of man's evolution and caused a phylogenetic mutation.

Now let's look at the larger mutations, those caused by experiences of genius, during the last three thousand years. The religious geniuses were followed by those of Greek civilization: Socrates, Plato, Aristotle, Zeno, Parmenides, Euripides, Sophocles, Euclid, Archimedes, Appolonius, Pappus, Menelaus, and a large number of other geometers. The geniuses of the European renaissance include: Chaucer, Shakespeare, Michaelangelo, Raphael, Rubens, Carravaggio, Titian, Dante, Milton, Cervantes, Leonardo, Kepler, Copernicus, Goethe, Heine, Moliere, Racine, Descartes, Hooke, Boyle, Bacon and so on. Post-renaissance the number greatly increases. This includes: Newton, Leibniz, Beethoven, Mozart, Bach, Haydn, Brahms, Schubert, Tolstoy, Dostoievsky, Chekov, Tchaichovsky, Stravinsky, Gounod, Moussorgsky, Sibelius, Maxwell, Faraday, Gauss, Darwin, Lamarck, Thompson, Clausius, Planck, Einstein, Schrodinger, Heisenberg, Bohr, Dirac, Born, de Broglie, Neumann, Shostakovich, R. Strauss, Elgar, Keats, Shelley, Coleridge, Blake, Wordsworth, Stevenson, Yeats, Shaw, Wilde, Eliot, Doyle, Brontes, Lawrence, Lamartine, Verdi, Rossini, Puccini, Bartok, Debussy, Hugo, Ravel, Chopin, Liszt, Dickens, Scott, Burns, Balzac, Ibsen, Picasso, Proust, Degas, Monet, Manet, Kant, Hegel, Marx, Schopenhauer, Heidegger, Russell, Euler, Cantor, Popper, Britten, Walton, Williams, Wells, Copland, Gershwin, Bernstein, Mark Twain (S. Clemens), Lewis Carrol (A. Dodgson), Poe, and so on. It is evident even from this cursory examination of only one kind of mutation, that the number of mutations in the human species, during a mere three thousand years, is vastly in excess of even the maximum estimate of Darwinian evolution and constitutes an hierarchical difference in scale. The total number of mutations during even a few thousand years, though difficult to estimate, can be seen to be extremely large, large enough to construct the house of evolution.

20

HIERARCHICAL
LEVELS OF CONSCIOUSNESS

As mentioned earlier, although Darwin's book is entitled *On The Origin of Species* it fails to discover the origin of any species. It is impossible for his theory to do so since all species are created discontinuously. A law of the logic of life states that there are different levels of consciousness of experience, feeling being the lowest. Experiences at different levels create different relations with the universe and reality; the relation with the universe and reality, which an experience creates, implies all the relations created by experiences at lower levels. Since the reduction of the wave-function and, hence, the physical nature of a particle, can only be understood in terms of consciousness at a higher level of organisation than the particle, this implies that relations created by experiences at lower levels can only be understood and defined in terms of experiences at higher levels. Consciousness, the structure of an experience, identifies the experience, because logically an organisation is identified by its structure. Feeling, touching and seeing create a relation with the universe and reality by identifying their consciousness with something that exists in the universe. The consciousness of an experience exists only in time (experiences exist only in time). Feeling identifies its consciousness with the feeling as a whole, which also exists in time. When we say we know a feeling we mean that we know the consciousness of the feeling, which we identify with the feeling as a whole. By this act of identification, feeling creates an existential (ontological) relation with the universe and reality. Feeling, when unknown, also creates this ontological relation.

A life selects a set of non-invariant tactile relations to create a set of invariant tactile relations, a set of tactile consciousness, which identifies an experience of touching. The consciousness of touching is a set of invariant tactile relations, which organises a set of feelings at a lower level of organisation than touching. The invariance is under time translation. The experience of touching identifies itself with its consciousness, which exists only in time. Touching identifies its consciousness, which exists only in time, with an identical set of object(-ive) consciousness, which exists in space, out there in the spatial universe. One consciousness set is identical to the other; touching identifies itself with the set in time and the set in time with the identical set in space. This does not mean that touching identifies itself with its spatial consciousness. Identification is intransitive. It thereby creates a relation of negation between itself and the universe and reality; it establishes there is something which is not itself, namely its consciousness which exists in space (as well as in time), as being distinct from itself. The latter consciousness exists solely in time. The intransitivity of identification can be seen in a comical way. Suppose identical twins, Bob and Mike, want to confuse the teacher. Bob, in class, identifies himself with Mike and Mike identifies himself with Bob. If the relation were transitive this would mean that Bob identifies himself with Bob and Mike with Mike, which is false. So the relation is intransitive.

Analogous to atoms organizing particles, touching organises feeling. Analogous to molecules organizing atoms, seeing organises touching. The ascending levels of organisation of particle, atom and molecule are analogous to the ascending levels of organisation of feeling, touching and seeing. To create seeing, a life selects a set of non-invariant visual relations to create a set of invariant visual relations, the set of visual consciousness, which identifies an experience of seeing. The consciousness of seeing is a set of invariant visual relations which organises a set of tactile experiences. The invariance is with respect to time translation. It identifies its consciousness, which exists in time, with a set of objective invariant visual relations, which exists out there in the universe in three-dimensional space. Being at a higher level of consciousness than touching, seeing creates a higher relation with the universe and reality. It creates a relation of independence: the universe and reality are experienced as being independent of seeing. The independence relation implies the relations of negation and existence (but not inversely), created by touching and feeling, because it is a higher order relation, created at a more advanced stage of evolution.

Did Macbeth, in Shakespeare's play, Macbeth, really see Banquo? Is there a real act of seeing involved in a hallucination? No. Did he really see anything? Macbeth cognitively recalled the set of real invariant visual relations, the visual consciousness of Banquo, which exists only in time. This was a real experience of memory. He identified this set, not with the real set of objectival (bodily) invariant visual consciousness relations of Banquo, existing in space, since Banquo, being dead, did not exist; but with an imagined set of non-invariant visual relations, existing only in time, which he imaginatively projects into space, that is, an hallucination. This does not symbolise reality, because it does not exist in space, as well as in time, so its structural relations are not invariant. He did not really see anything. Macbeth wrongly applied the law of identification. He did not have a visual experience: he experienced a hallucination. This appears to be paradoxical. How can a real consciousness identify something unreal? To identify something is not to establish an identity with that something. Remember how, in linguistic theory, a connotation is not identical to the concept which it identifies. This illustration only touches on complex issues but it serves to give some indication of the power of the concept of consciousness in answering difficult questions of perception. This is an example of a real existent, remembered visual consciousness which exists in time, being identified with an unreal existent, a hallucination, which is falsely presumed to exist in space. Banquo's ghost does not exist in space but only in time as it is created in Macbeth's imagination and exists solely in his imagination. Are there unreal existents which do exist in space? Television pictures, Mirror images, rainbows and holograms are examples of unreal existents which exist in space. To observe a mirror image is to identify a known set of real invariant visual consciousness relations, the subjectivity of the experience, which exists in time, with the image, which is a set of unreal invariant visual consciousness relations that exist in space. The observer is having a real visual experience because the image, unreally, does exist in space. [To say that it unreally exists is not to say that it does not really exist. The first use of (un)really is a scientific use of the word whereas the second use of really is its use in spoken language. The first use is predicative of existence (refuting Kant), while the second use is for emphasis in the false denial of existence.] The image exists unreally and not really because it has no objective properties which symbolise reality. The image is not a figment of the imagination, like a hallucination, which does not exist in space but only in time. Not even Macbeth claimed to see Banquo's ghost in a mirror! A real visual experience only occurs if the visual consciousness of the experience is identified with a real or unreal object which exists in space. Since the image is unreal, it does not exist in the universe, which is the set of all real things. So to what set of things does the image belong? It exists in the mind. The mind is real and exists in the universe but the existential relation is not transitive. Unreal things do not exist in the universe. This power to create the unreal which is not in the universe would seem to be miraculous. Even god could only create a universe of real things, but real things create unreal things as part of the creative process, so that it is reality (god if you like to think of it that way), that is the prime mover. What is unreal must have some connection with the real. An elephant with ten heads can only be imagined because there are elephants and there are heads. To use an ancient argument, could god really be regarded as perfect if there was something he could not create. In other words, is god perfect if he created man, who is a creature that can create unreal things, things which god could not create on his own? So man is essential to the idea of the perfection of god as a being who requires man as an integral part of the universal creative process. The mirror image relation has been studied by ethologists and psychologists in order to produce a theory of mind for animals and children. Darwin, ahead of his time, examined the reaction of higher primates to their image in a mirror. He found that they were puzzled and annoyed. Their sense of reality was disturbed. What looks and acts like a fellow primate did not even have a real existence, either in front of, or behind, the mirror. It has since been discovered that chimpanzees, the most intelligent of the higher primates, do recognise their own bodies in a mirror image. This was discovered by a psychologist, Gordon Gallup. He marked a red spot on the forehead of a chimp which he placed in front of a mirror. The chimp acted as if it knew the reflection was its own; it touched the red spot on its forehead. From this it has been falsely concluded by some that chimps have a self-conscious mind. The correct interpretation of this experiment is that chimps know the image correspondence relation between an object and its image. Animals with mind know the causal relation between sensory experiences but do not know the logical law of causality, which this relation obeys, since animals do not know laws of nature. Chimps and orangutans are exceptional in knowing the very difficult image relation, but they do not know the image law of logic which this relation obeys. This bodily recognition does not mean they are self-conscious. Not even all the species of man, the genus Homo, are self-conscious, for example Homo habilis. Very young children, tested in this way, are also found to recognise their own bodies. Notwithstanding, contrary to the opinion of their doting parents, they are not self-conscious, only becoming so when they learn the logical laws of morality.

Another category of experience of the unreal which is very important for psychology and cognitive science is that of optical illusions. They are as profoundly significant as they are entertaining. The attempts to explain them have been physiological and cognitive. The former have failed, while the latter, because of a misplaced emphasis on the importance of perspective have also failed. They are explained cognitively by relating them to the logical laws of the universe. This is done for the best known illusions which have received most attention in the literature. The others tend to be more complex and more difficult to explain but the principle of explanation is the same.

The best known optical illusion is the Muller-Lyer illusion. There is a pair of arrows whose shafts are of equal length. One arrow has outgoing and the other ingoing arrowheads at each end. The one with outgoing heads looks considerably longer, though it is of the same length. The relation between the real geometric lengths of the lines obeys the logical law of symmetry under change of relata, because they are of the same length. The mind thinks that the relation between the lengths obeys the law of asymmetry under change of relata, because it is confused by a double application of the law of symmetry under inversion. The relation between the fins at the end of each arrow (each arrow taken separately), obeys symmetry under inversion, and similarly the relation between the fins at the top of each arrow and the relation between the fins at the bottom of each arrow. The mind just cannot cope with certain combinations of logic, so it knowingly selects the logic which it can handle, at the expense of the other. The theory does not explain why it is the figure with the outgoing fins which looks longer. No theory explains everything. The outgoing fins constitute an extension so, intuitively it is to be expected the figure with them should look longer. If the fins are replaced by buckets the explanation is still valid, which is not so for perspectival explanations. The illusion emphasises the top-down relation of causality in perception. When the mind cannot dissociate the logic of asymmetry and symmetry but must conjoin them, the eye has no option but to perceive asymmetry where there is none. The symmetrical relation causes the asymmetrical relation, hence the illusion. It is primarily our mind not our eyes which determines the creative nature of our perception. That it is symmetry under inversion, which does the causing, is evident. Suppose the line with the out-going fins looked the correct length and the other line looked shorter than it should; or conversely, suppose the line with the in-going fins looked the correct length but the other line looked longer than it should. Then we could not be sure as to the cause of the illusion. But one line looks longer, and the other shorter, than it should. The nature of the illusion obeys symmetry under inversion, so this law must be the cause of the illusion.

The second example is the Ponzo or railway lines illusion. The cross line in the narrower part of the space enclosed by the converging lines looks longer than the other cross line although they are the same length. The same line continues to look longer in whichever orientation the figure is viewed. The explanation is that the relation between the converging lines obeys symmetry under inversion, the lines being symmetrical about a line which joins the mid-points of the two cross lines. This confuses the mind, since it cannot also apply another symmetry law, namely the law of symmetry under change of relata, obeyed by the relation between the two cross lines. Instead it wrongly applies the law of asymmetry under change of relata.

The third exmple is the Poggendorf illusion. Two horizontal parallel lines are crossed at about forty-five degrees to the vertical by a straight line which is broken in the space between the parallel lines. The two pieces of this straight line do not appear to form a straight line. The explanation for the illusion is similar to the Ponzo except that the law in both cases is the law of symmetry under change of relata, neither relation obeying symmetry under inversion. The mind cannot deal with the double application of symmetry under change of relata obeyed by the relation between the parallels and the relation between the two parts of the transversal. So it falsely interprets the latter as obeying asymmetry under change of relata. The classical illusion figures, the Hering, Orbison and Zollner can be similarly explained by a confusion resulting from the application of symmetry under inversion and symmetry under change of relata. Let's look at illusions which are not distortion illusions. These sometimes arise from the application of a single logical law of the universe.

In the well known case of the urn there are two choices depending on what one chooses as object and figure. Since we read black print (object) on a white background, if the urn is black we see an urn and miss the white faces; but if the urn is white we see black faces and miss the urn. Strictly speaking this is not an illusion of ambiguity, since it is safe to bet on which of the two possible choices one is expected to choose. One could even imagine the artist to be unaware he had created an ambiguity. But it is a picturesque illustration of what is meant by an illusion of ambiguity.

The duck-rabbit illusion is a result of two possible choices, which are related by the law of asymmetry under change of relata. Again there is only one law involved but it is a law of asymmetry not symmetry. The eye and the neck are common to both figures but everything else is changed; for example the duck's bill is the rabbit's pair of ears. Besides being an optical illusion this is a work of art. It is two pictures in one. Do not be seduced by relativistic interpretation into thinking that you are not looking at two real works of art. It is a law of artistic logic (and a very strange one) that an organ as complex and as important as the eye can be represented by a mere dot. It is also a law of logic that, in profile, the side of the head to which the eye is nearer is the front of the head. The picture is a set of such invariant (under time translation) acausal logical relations. The relations are acausal because if you draw the nose first it determines the position of the eye and inversely. This is true whatever interpretation, rabbit or duck, is made of the content of the picture. Either way it is a work of art. If the artist did not intend two pictures, is the unintended picture still a work of art? No. But it becomes a work of art if interpreted as such, created by the mind of the interpreter, though not by the artist. To perceive a work of art requires an intellectual effort of logical interpretation. In the creative effort of understanding there will be non-invariant interpretations as well as invariant. Only the invariant will survive and contribute to the evolving cumulative cultural understanding of the artistic work. We owe our ability to produce this understanding to higher religious experience. For example, our evolving interpretation of the paradoxes of the Eden myth and the paradoxical parables of Christ. They have also given us the ability to create the host of scientific and philosophical paradoxes whose solution points the direction of future scientific evolution.

An illusion is a creative act. Sometimes the mind will apply a law of logic to fill up an "empty conceptual space". This is true of the phantom triangle, which is constructed because cognition abhors a vacuum. A false interpretation is, in this case, better than none at all. Fascinatingly, there are no triangles in the figure but if you were to ask someone from memory to say how many triangles they saw in the illusion (a trick question!), they would probably say two. The mind applies symmetry under inversion to the "real triangle" to produce the inverted phantom triangle, because the three "triangular" vertices, which exist on their own, have an actual existence. As we have seen, in the other illu-

185

sions the mind loves the duality of symmetry-asymmetry, with no regard for the truth, so here also we have asymmetry under change of relata, which takes the wonderful form of the compelling glow of the phantom triangle. The illusion is not just about figures but about the intensity of vision. A complete account of such an illusion no doubt requires a physiological as well as a logical, that is, a cognitive explanation, each throwing light on the other.

If you mark a face of a Necker cube with a small circle the figure alternates in depth; the face sometimes appears as the front and sometimes as the back. The circle jumps from one position to the other. Perception is not determined solely by the objective two-dimensional geometrical pattern of the lines on the page. It is determined by the subjective three-dimensional interpretation of the observer. There is a dynamic searching for the best interpretation. It is not just in illusions that this happens. It also happens in normal vision when we always wish to, and usually do, arrive at a unique solution. As with all experiences, no matter how small the organism, selection is a learning process. The unique solution, an invariant visual relation, cannot appear by chance. In this case, as with other ambiguous illusions, no invariant solution is possible. If you want your sight to evolve don't spend all your time looking at illusionary phenomena. The world is a world of consciousness created by our perceptions; when we create invariant relations we evolve, if not we must go on searching for the correct answers. Just as a mathematician has to keep on trying to find the answer so does an animal trying to create the experience of seeing. It is a learning process. There is no easy road. What we are now was created by the unremitting efforts of billions of organisms. Animals also experience illusions since their selection process also obeys laws of logic and their selections are subject to interpretation. But animals do not know the laws of logic so they cannot create illusions and cannot argue about their nature or, indeed, about anything else.

Support for this interpretation of illusions comes from the interpretation of dyslexia. It is common to many dyslexics that they cannot distinguish on the printed page between the letters p, b, and d. It is not difficult to see why, since a mere inspection of their shapes makes it evident. The relation between p and b obeys symmetry under inversion. (The inversion is about a horizontal axis.) The relation between b and d also obeys this law (for inversion about a vertical axis). These relations are mathematical yet dyslexics who are good mathematicians also experience this difficulty. Our theory explains why. The logical laws of mathematics are not identical to the logical laws of the universe. The law of symmetry under inversion is both a logical law of mathematical language and a logical law of the universe. In its application, visually to these letters, it is a logical law of the universe, not a logical law of mathematical language. A dyslexic either cannot apply this law to these letters correctly for purely cognitive reasons or for a combination of cognitive and psycho-physiological reasons.

The argument from illusion is important in the representationist realist philosophy of knowledge. Those who believe this philosophy are piggy in the middle between the Scylla of naïve realism and the Charybdis of idealism or its mad extension of solipsism. Representationists believe that we do not experience material objects directly (as do naïve realists) but that we only have direct perception of subjective impressions. Their problem is that they have no way of showing that there is a similarity between the impression and the real object of which it is an impression. With their emphasis on the importance of subjective perception, they court solipsism. They need a logical bridge to cross over the bog of solipsism, to the dry land of objective realism. This requires a new logic, the logical laws of the universe, in particular the logical law of identification, which identifies the properties of visual consciousness with the properties of the real visual object in space. The properties of sense-data (private impressions), the so-called secondary properties, are no less real than the primary properties of physics (mass, length etc.). When we perceive a book to be red it is because the book has the property of being red (in that given light context). It is a property of the book not just a property of our perception alone. The cognitive perception of the book's length is also context dependent, in a relativistic sense.

Consistent with Husserl's philosophy, the universe must be seen as a universe of consciousness, existing at different levels. The universe is not the reality which is, it is a physical reality, which exists, and which symbolises the former; universal consciousness symbolises reality. The real things of the universe symbolise reality. For Kant the universe is reality, as it was for Spinoza. (Spinoza also thought, monistically, that god manifested himself as universe) The "appearances" Kant speaks of, the experiential inventions (phenomena) by which we relate our life to the universe, are, in his philosophy, ways of apprehending the universe, whose real nature, the thing-in-itself, remains hidden behind an impenetrable veil. The Kantian dichotomy, between phenomenon and noumenon, creates, not so much a theory of knowledge, as a theory of the impossibility of knowledge. The present theory does not merely substitute an unknowable reality for Kant's unknowable universe. The universe is apprehensible at all levels of experience, because we construct the universe as consciousness, as already described. This consciousness is logically related to unknowable reality also, whereas in Kant's philosophy, experience is unrelated to reality. This is why it is not possible to create a theory of knowledge with Kant's philosophy. Kant thought that the deeper reality behind "appearances" is the universe as it really is and not just the way it appears because of the contingency of our biological and psychical construction. In the present theory, the universe is not reality: there is, behind the universe, an absolute, unknowable reality, which is symbolised by the objects of the universe, which is the stuff, consciousness, of our everyday experience. This is the real "stuff" of the universe. It is knowable through the concept of invariance, as suggested by Ernst Cassirer, since invariant things and relations symbolise reality. Schopenhauer, Fichte, and others understood that Kant's philosophy was incomplete, since it was necessary to relate our experience to reality. Schopenhauer's failed attempt to do so, in the nineteenth century, was misunderstood and misinterpreted, by a reductionist obsessed culture which in the twentieth century ridiculed his unique contribution to philosophy. This was also the fate of the great philosopher, Heidegger, who, amidst the raging storm of fanatical scepticism of the twentieth century, attempted to steer philosophy back to its traditional ontological quest.

There are two kinds of consciousness: subjective (experiential), existing only in time, and objective, existing also in space. Both are real, being sets of invariant relations which symbolize reality. Subjective does not mean unreal. Only organisms are creative, identifying their subjective consciousness with the objective consciousness of the objects of the universe. Objective consciousness, the consciousness of objects of the universe, existed before the origin of life. The triangular relation between subjectivity, objectivity and reality is discovered by the evolution of physics. Truth is absolute. Subjective and objective truth are both absolute. Jacob Bronowski, physicist-philosopher, (author of *The Ascent of Man*) was fond of saying, "There is no absolute truth". Name this proposition Q. There are two possibilities (a) Q is absolutely true. If so, it is not absolutely true, since it says so. So, Q is self-contradictory. (b) Q is not absolutely true so it may be there is absolute truth (even though Q itself cannot be so). What he is really saying is that absolute truth may exist after all and he means that absolutely, that is, contradictorily! We have two contradictions for the price of one. He who challenges truth speaks with fork in mouth. The challenge to the scientist is to assert its existence by defining it. If the bird of truth doesn't sing who shall be so foolish, or so obstinate, as to criticize its song. This doesn't mean it doesn't have a song. It is the onus and responsibility of the scientist to define truth and the responsibility of his critics to await his definition in silence. Karl Popper was influential in persuading scientists that absolute truth is uanattainable. Truth lies at the end of the rainbow, one fine day you may aspire to it, get nearer and nearer to it, but ultimately, every proposition is falsifiable. You can only meet truth at an asymptotic infinity. The seductive maiden of truth loves to flirt, but she will never marry. But truth, in order to define herself was only awaiting the correct suitor to define himself. The name of the suitor is reality.

As evolution progresses in the biosphere, life diversifies, as more possibilities open up for the development of consciousness. Biological evolution is the evolution of sets of consciousness and the biophysical structures which they cause. Life and body are inseparable, in a symbiotic relationship. The reason your behaviour, which affects your body macroscopically, causes changes in hereditary DNA is because causality works from the top down, from the level of feeling to the level of molecule. The rate of evolution of the biosphere changed, discontinuously, in the Cambrian era about 560 million years ago. After 3000 million years from the origin of life, the earth had only produced small, multicellular, unsegmented animals. The Cambrian produced an explosive variety of segmented forms. Why? Our theory can convincingly explain this.

Whenever there is a discontinuity in the level of consciousness of experience, there is a discontinuity in the rate of creation of life, and so, a discontinuity in the evolution of the biosphere with the creation of new species. It follows that during the Cambrian, the experience of touching was emergently formed. It is this which produced the evolutionary explosion. Gould says that the change was far greater than any other change of its kind. The truth is the reverse. The higher the level of experience, the greater the change. The later creation of seeing produced a far larger discontinuity than touching, while the creation of knowing, of mind, produced a still greater evolutionary discontinuity. The evolution of mind offered up still further possibilities of discontinuity; unconscious, to conscious, to self-conscious. The discontinuities were not just in the elements of the mind set, the cognitive experiences, but in the set (the whole set) itself, the mind, which is a set of cognitive experiences.

Darwinism says there was lots of time for evolution which is continuous, but also says that for most of the time there is no evolution, when environmental adaptation has reached an equilibrium optimal state. So there wasn't plenty of time after all. And evolution wasn't continuous - what about the Cambrian which blatantly contradicts the continuity of evolution? Dawkins, as usual, buries his head in the sand and tries to explain away the importance of the Cambrian. So how did evolution really happen: nearly all of significant evolution happened in a remarkably short period of 560 million years, not the thousands of millions that we thought before. It may take a long time to bake a cake – but look at the size of the cake. Then it galloped, after the Cambrian, with discontinuously longer strides. Evolution is not a slow, continuous process as Darwinists would have you believe: it is a discontinuous, rapid process, with ever-larger discontinuities in rate. Look at the size of the cake before you use the word slow. With man, the evolutionary process becomes in effect just that - the evolution of man, galloping, at a unilaterally increasing rate, "to infinity". Man is not the here-today-gone-tomorrow creature which Darwinists suppose him to be: he is the ultimate form of evolution in the universe, the culmination of the entire process. He is evolution become conscious of itself, deterministically directing itself, by discovering its laws. He is creating the highest level of experience, which organises the level below it, just as preceding levels have done in the past, to create a higher level of experience. Artists have a much better understanding of evolution than Darwinists. For Sophocles and Shakespeare, man is an amazing animal; for the latter he is the "paragon of animals". For G. B. Shaw, "To be in hell is to drift; to be in heaven is to steer". Shakespeare understood the relation between contingency and necessity: "There is a divinity that shapes our end, rough-hew it how we will". For Darwinism, contingency is the beginning, middle and end.

21

CONCLUSIONS

This is a quantum-relativistic theory of the origin of
life. It is also a unified theory of science: of logic, physics,
biolgy, psychology, linguistics and mathematics. The most
impo tant single idea of the theory is that life originated as
a result of a combination of the two different kinds of CPT
violation. There was an immensely long progressive evolution of symmetry violation before this, beginning with particles, to produce atom, molecule, and macromolecule; but
this dual combined violation (C or P but not T; and C, P, T)
was the final, determining step which made life inevitable
and the next step up the progressive evolutionary ladder.
It is clear from this that the experimental creation of life is
still some time away. It is more difficult; both theoretically
and experimentally, than we at first assumed but it is by
no means unattainable. It is no less evident that this goal,
having been physically defined, will certainly be achieved.
All scientific evolutionary paths converge on the origin of
life. The claim of our theory is that, just as at the beginning
of the twentieth century Planck and Einstein began a new
era of quantum and relativistic physics, our theory begins,
by a remarkable coincidence, a new era of unified science,
including unified physics at the beginning of this century.
Our theory creates an ontology for science which Einstein
always believed to be necessary. All science is metaphysi-

cal. Every science attempts to discover the nature of absolute scientific truth. Truth is defined in our theory in terms of a defined absolute reality which is transcendental, but not Kantian, though pioneered by Kant. The philosophy of reductionism is replaced by one of constructive integration, since the former —despite its notable successes—is inadequate for the formation of a theory of evolution. The theory unifies and defines the concepts of reality, truth, law, fact, word, concept, meaning, definition, force, causality, metric, wavefunction, energy, inertia, entropy, work, heat, conservation, non-conservation, particle, atom, molecule, life, experience, feeling, free will, heat, work, macro and supramacro-molecule. By unifying these with the concept of consciousness by defining the reduction of the wavefunction in terms of a defined consciousness, physics is unified with psychology and biology. Biological evolution, ontogenetic and phylogenetic, is the evolution of consciousness. The evolution of bodily structures is caused by the evolution of time-structured functional process, which is the evolution of consciousness.

Our theory begins with a theory of knowledge. This is based on a set of ontological logical laws. These define the concepts of reality, truth, law and fact. This enables scientific concepts in general to be defined, including in linguistic theory, the definition of define. The activity of universal science is defined as the creation of a set of structural laws of the universe, expressed in defined concepts, by deducing them from a set of logical laws of the universe whose consistency is assumed. A law is absolutely true, being defined in terms of an absolute reality. Although scientists of a rationalist philosophy, Einstein for example, have been deducing universal structural laws from logical laws of the universe, they have been unable to distinguish between logical and structural law. Consequently they have not realised that they have been deducing propositions that are true; that is, *proven* to be true and not just testable propositions which may ultimately be invalidated by experiment. Their failure to do so has spawned an extreme form of neo-empericism which is now the prevailing philosophy among physicists of the modern age.

It says that the mathematical representation of a physical entity (the mathematical equation) contains the ultimate source of truth about that entity. One ventures beyond the mathematics at ones peril. Mathematics is so profound that it embodies the very nature of universal truth. It is, so to speak, the language of god. The human mind seeks to understand, to explain the universe by asking: "What does the mathematics mean?" It selects one from among many possible philosophical interpretations of the equation, as the one which is not contradicted by experiment. They are concerned only with what works. The interpretation is not regarded as being absolutely true, as future experiment may prove it false. The ultimate meaning of the mathematics is beyond human understanding, only god knows. Universal science so described is really philosophical – mathematical science and not really universal science. The reason such philosophers are quick to accuse others of being "merely philosophers" and not universal scientists is because they wish to forestall criticism. They regard absolute truth and proven proposition to exist only in mathematics (mathematical language) but only in a philosophical sense, since the absoluteness of the truth of certain statements such as 2+2=4, seem self evident. Mathematical truth is undefined and because of the Godel propositions, scientifically undefinable within a system of mathematics. Truth is conceived to exist purely on philosophical ground and to be unrelated to the universe. Scientists of this persuasion have deceived themselves into thinking that they have made great strides in science. Can anyone really say that with endless descriptions of black holes, worm holes and dark matter they have a better understanding of the universe because of such theories?

The existence of defined scientific truth as distinct from undefined philosophical truth can only be postulated in universal, not in purely mathematical science. Proof, the deduction of absolutely true conclusions, exists in universal as well as in mathematical science. Mathematicians have always thought that they alone were capable of proof.

Our theory unifies the electromagnetic and gravitational forces. Other theories stumble at this obstacle, including the much vaunted, but unrealistic, supersymmetry theory, which is tall on claim (not to mention obscurity and incoherence) but short on achievement.

We claim our theory is profound; it does not wallow in superficiality, as does Darwinism, with its endless just-so stories and its futile statistical "explanations", based on derring-do logic, evading the real problems of evolution. We have grown tired of Darwinists endlessly brandishing their totem-pole aphorisms with little or nothing to show for it. Competition is evident and important but not a profound explanation of evolution. The brick of so enormously organised an edifice as evolution cannot be made of chance. It requires logical naivety of the highest order and a grievous lack of understanding or recognition of the profundity of the phenomenon of life, to believe so. It is reminiscent of Descartes who thought that a dog was just a machine. Now Darwinists, justifiably called fundamentalist, say a man is just a machine. Reductionism gone mad. Darwin fails where a true theory must be expected to succeed. It gives a superficial answer to the goal of purposeful behaviour: survival. The true goal is maximization of life, which often prejudices survival; for example, human and other animal activity often make survival irrelevant as, for example, kamikaze pilots, who try to maximize their lives by anticipating and enjoying glory, prestige and honour. Chance alone, cannot explain the steady, step by step, accumulation of organisation, needed for the origin of life; Darwinists give a science-fiction type of explanation of this: life came from outer space; of course it did, just like the "thing". Darwinists are correct in seeking the cause of life within the organism and not mysticism, but they make the same mistake as Boltzmann in physics, in not seeking a micro explanation for a macro phenomenon. The most important flaw in Darwinism is that it cannot produce a single favourable mutation. This is ample reason, in itself, to abandon the theory. Consequently, it cannot lead to a theory of development nor logically, a theory of phylogeny. One can no more explain life purely macroscopically than one can explain magnetism without particle theory (electron spin). But chemical molecular theory is not enough; it must be a particle interaction theory, a physical theory.

The status of quantum theory has been questioned for nearly a century, not least by Einstein. Make no mistake. Physics is quantum-relativity; it is here to stay. The present theory has transformed and supplemented quantum logic. Its biggest problem, the misnamed measurement problem, really that of reduction of the wavefunction, as suspected by John Bell, can only be solved if the concept of measurement is excluded from the formulation of the laws of logic: measurement is not a defined concept. A measurement is *not* required to produce a reduction of the wavefunction. A reduction occurs when the property corresponding to the superposed function becomes knowable. (It reduces if known, because it is then knowable, but no observer is necessary). The wavefunction represents physical reality: it is a combined gravo-electromagnetic field, not just a computing device.

It has long been considered that it is necessary to add asymmetric terms to the wave equation. The problem is to find which asymmetric terms apply in a particular context. Our theory, being contextual in its application, has discovered the nature of these contexts; e.g. molecular interactions have terms which violate CP and T. When the superposed wavefunction solution of the wave equation violates T, reduction occurs. This condition arises, naturally, from thermodynamic theory. Heisenberg understood that reduction was in some way connected to the irreversibility of thermodynamic process. The eigenstate represents a symmetric interaction and is energy conserved; the superposed state represents an asymmetric interaction and is energy non-conserved. This leads to an explanation of the second law of thermodynamics in terms of micro interactions. The "arrow" of time is seen to be a consequence of T violation. We confidently assert that once this is understood there can be no doubt that this aspect of the problem of time is resolved. The "arrow" is also a biological (but not an astrophysical) "arrow". To prove this requires the theory of the origin of life, which is obtained by analogy with the quantum-thermodynamical theory. The theory also proves momentum non-conservation of (some) asymmetric interactions. This produces a quantum-relativistic formulation of Newton's laws which physically determine the conditions for linear and nonlinear geometry. Both kinds of geometry are real in their correct physical context. (Kant was not entirely wrong, as the empiricists have assumed.) This unifies mathematics with physics. The greatest problem of mechanics: What is the nature of the "inertial" force? the "phantom" force with us since Newton, is resolved: it is a gravitational force, the result of momentum non-conservation for the gravitational force in nonlinear space. Einstein thought the force to be gravity but his Machian "explanation" borders on mysticism. What is mass? How is it produced? Not by Higgs bosons for there is no such particle. Our theory gives a convincing explanation of mass and inertia. Mass is a property and energy a thing. Mass, when it exists, is the measure of the energy of a particle. If an isolated particle were not acted on by a self-force and did accelerate, the concept of inertia would be meaningless. An isolated particle obeys Newton's first law and is not acted on by a self-force, so the concept of inertia is meaningful. It means that when a particle interacts, because of nonlinear superposition, it resists a change of motion with the entire energy of the wavefunction, that is, with its mass. Newton had an isolated macrosystem in mind in forming the momentum conservation laws. Since all bodies have inertia, the force on a body, in a noninertial ("accelerated") frame (one in which, classically, Newton's law of inertia is not valid), must be an inertial force. Schizophrenically, the frame with, to all appearances, no inertia exhibited, has inertial forces. Yet there are no external interacting bodies. Einstein says the stars are the external bodies. Our theory says there are no external bodies so the concept of an isolated system is valid; this means the momentum conservation law is only valid contextually. An isolated body (macrosystem) produces its own self-gravitational force, because of momentum non-conservation of gravity in nonlinear space. There is a most curious and interesting analogy between the theoretical errors of Darwin and Einstein. In Darwin's theory, the answer is to be found, not in selection from without the organism, not in natural selection by the environment, but from within; while in Einstein's theory, the answer is to be found, not in the stars, but within the body. Natural selection is not natural, nor is it selection. An isolated system does not interact with the stars, so any theory in which interaction is primary must discount the Einstein explanation of inertial force as sheer humbug. The Bohm theory is also a realist field theory, but there is no wave reduction in his theory; so it has the weakness of the Everett multi-universe theory, which is strong on universes but weak on logic. The logic of the present theory requires that there be only one universe and one reality. An infinity of independent universes would require the assumption of an infinity of independent realities, which is a retrograde step to neo-Kantian philosophy. This is a problem in universal logic, not structural physics as is generally believed. The Everett postulate is false, interesting, even fascinating, but for all that, it must be said, completely crazy. The universe is the set of all real things; there cannot be more than one set of all real things. It is a sad reflection on the state of modern logical thinking that the Everett hypothesis is so popular. It could be that it is not popular among physicists so much as astrophysicists who think the universe has a wavefuntion.

Since Aristotle, there has been surprisingly little advance in logic. We consider the present revolution in logic to be the most considerable advance yet made. It is the first scientific theory of knowledge. To understand its magnitude it is essential to consider the evolution of logic since the higher religions evolved. The ability of modern man to reason, philosophically and scientifically, in spoken mathematical language, derives entirely from religious experience. It is only by kicking against the womb of traditional religious experience that scientific logical thinking evolved. The train of structural science runs on the fuel of logic. When the axiomatic fuel runs out, the deductive consequences of a logical set being limited, further evolving sets are needed. Maxwell in thermodynamics, Einstein with relativity, Neumann and Dirac, with quantum theory, introduced sets of universal logic. Darwin also did so. The level of scientific consciousness was too low for them to realise they were logical sets. Logic had not yet learned to look at itself in the mirror. (The laws of quantum theory used to be called "rules".)

The present theory introduces a new kind of logic: logical laws of the universe; that is, it raises the consciousness of the use of such sets. They have been known for a few million years (!) without being expressed. But they are new, in the sense that their level of consciousness is new: the logic is defined, the natural structural laws they cause are therefore defined, since the concepts with which they are expressed are defined. They enable the structural laws to be rationally deduced, just as in mathematics, theorems are deduced from a set of axioms. This realises the dream of Plato and Descartes. The age of philosophical reductionist pessimism is at an end; we can no longer neglect the rationalist philosophy of Plato, Aristotle, Descartes, Leibniz, Kant, Einstein, or the nonreductionist philosophy of Bergson, Teilhard, Whyte, Bertalanffy, Heidegger, or Cassirer.

The theory explains how knowledge is produced and

explains what logical knowledge is. Mathematicians have always thought that they, alone, reason logically; the universal scientist was thought to rely, for the most part, on intuition or guessing, but the method of obtaining knowledge has always been the same for both. In mathematics, from a set of axioms there is deduced, by the logical law of (noncausal) implication, a set of theorems; in structural science a set of logical laws of the universe is formed from which there is deduced, by the logical law of causal implication (causality), a set of structural universal laws. The laws of the universe, like mathematical theorems, are deduced mathematically from a set of axioms. The universe, à la Descartes, can be deduced from the comfort of your armchair. The structural laws of the universe relate to sensory experience by observation to produce new ground for the formation of new logical universal laws. The latter are freely made postulates (as Einstein insisted), the products of human imagination, and are logically related to absolute reality by a symbolic relation. The logical laws are uncaused, the structural laws of the universe are caused by the logical laws of the universe. A computer, despite claims to the contrary, has no mind, no logical thought, no imagination no feeling, no creativity, no free will: all it has is chips (with everything). You need not be concerned that computers will be disturbed by these accusations: they have no feelings, not a grain of sense or sensibility. Yet Marvin Minsky, David Dennett, Richard Dawkins and a host of others think that one day computers will supersede humans. Could it be that at this very moment computers are speculating, philosophically, on what it would be like to take over the world. The question is rhetorical: computers don't philosophise either. Minsky, needless to say, a reductionist, says that his brain is just a slab of meat. How sad. Considering how notable have been his contributions to cognitive science, one can only speculate with awe on what he could have achieved if he had a brain just like the rest of us.

The revolution in logic arises by defining the concept of causality, the bugbear of David Hume which quantum theory is generally thought to have eliminated. It is defined as a logically ordered paired relation of implication (which, most importantly, may or may not also be temporally ordered). Mathematical implication, which can only be defined by first defining causality, is defined analogously as a paired relation of implication which is not ordered. This unifies the two kinds of logic, explaining their common source of logical implication. The ability of logic to be logical about itself, to be self examining, was introduced by the great logician Kurt Godel with far-reaching consequences for our understanding of the concepts of truth and reality and of the future evolution of man. These are discovered by our theory. Many unsuccessful attempts to make fruitful use of the elusive and perplexing concept of reality have led some influential philosophers to regard truth as a trivial, even redundant concept (if you can't understand it, insult it). Our theory defines truth, reality, causal and acausal implication, thereby giving logic and knowledge a firm scientific, and not merely philosophical, foundation. So far, we have not understood whether logic is philosophy or science or neither; logic is science. The theory of knowledge arises from the great philosophies of Aristotle, Kant and Husserl but is not, itself, merely philosophical. Therein lies its power to rigorously deduce the structural laws of the universe, which are thereby proven and known to be true in a scientifically defined sense of the word true.

The condition for reduction of the wavefunction, knowability, brings consciousness, as a scientific concept no less valid than energy, momentum or entropy, explicitly into physical science for the first time. Science is compelled to be objective about subjectivity. This is consistent with Husserl's philosophy. This has the disconcerting and seemingly illogical consequence that the human mind was implicit in the universe even when, in the course of its evolution, it contained only particles. We need not conjure up a preordaining personal god. But the consequence is logically inescapable: the predetermination of universal evolution solves some of its so far ineluctable problems. Why, for example, did the earth produce life so soon after cooling, contrary to Darwinian probabilism? It did so because life was deterministically inevitable, determined by law, just waiting for the right physical conditions. Why do macro and supramacro molecules exist? Because the universe is constructed mathematically; so it was only a matter of time before the correct invariant relations for CPT violating interactions came into existence. Qualitative discontinuities from particle to atom to molecule lead to discontinuities in size: ordinary to macro to supramacro, leading in turn to further qualitative discontinuities, experiences at different, ascending levels of organisation. Is it a contingent fact that primates (less than 10 million years ago) started walking upright? No. It was necessarily so, since man is preordained in the universe. So it was only a matter of time before some primate started to walk upright. Some will no doubt interpret predestination as tantamount to saying there is a personal mind, the mind of God, with a universal plan of creation. There is no personal god. Man, the sleeping giant with his newly found self-consciousness, must emerge from his three million year incubation period of scientific immaturity, don the mantle of creation and become master of the universe. This was predicted by Moses three thousand years ago.

This is the first theory to define scientific concepts. To do this it is first necessary to create the first linguistic theory which defines the concepts of meaning, word, concept, and definition. These are defined in terms of the undefined concept of connotation (Any conceptual language must have undefined concepts). There are two kinds of human conceptual language, spoken and mathematical, the latter being the language in which scientific concepts are expressed. The meaning of a word is a set of identifying connotations. In speech, a word concept has no defining

connotation; in science a word concept has a defining connotation, one which causes all the other connotations of the
concept. It is the vastly increased organizing power of
mathematical language which results from this that gives
man his ability to dominate the universe. The Fregean
Venus paradox, a century old, is resolved by our theory.
Civilization began, a few evolutionary moments ago, with
the discovery of mathematical language. The logic of this
linguistic theory is confined to that necessary to discover
the origin of life. To discover the evolution of higher levels
of experience requires the formation of further logical linguistic sets. The evolution of new structural laws must
always be preceded by, because caused by, the creation of
new logical sets. Since the origin of a prebiotic system is
also the origin of an encoding system, this implies that linguistic theory must be a theory of sets, because the former
also is as a result of the ontological evolution of sets that
preceded it in the course of evolution.

The theory contradicts Darwin's theory and replaces it.
In the latter, information passes entirely from DNA to protein, though experiment contradicts this (reverse transcription of RNA). Reverse flow of information lets in neo-
Lamarckism. All favourable mutations are caused by protein structures. A mutation cannot logically precede the protein structure which causes it. Creative change is causally
directed from protein to DNA. Feedback is directed from
DNA to protein. Darwin's theory cannot account for
favourable mutations. It is the life of the cell, since it is a set
of experiences, which creates invariant time-ordered functional structure. The life selects, at any time, which functions are to be operative and also selects which sets of
invariant time-ordered bases are to be used to encode protein structure. Feelings which are created by the life of the
cell by organising protein interactions, cause feelings as
time-ordered DNA mutations. They in turn, if selected by
the life of the cell, cause feelings which causally organise
the processes of transcription and translation producing

primary protein structure. Because of the huge entropy of the system, increasing unilaterally, this rapidly self-organises into a supramacromolecule. The more advanced the organism, the greater its entropy and the greater the speed with which it constructs its molecules; so the more complex the physical activities of which it is capable and the greater is its measure of life. An elephant gets more out of life than a moth or a frog. Let's abandon this egalitarian Darwinian nonsense; Darwinists are only interested in levelling down. If man is to be his true self, he must aspire to ever higher heights. The life acts as the memory of the organism, freely selecting which experiences, and therefore which functions are to be selected from the memory bank. An unconscious mind has cognitive memory, knowingly selecting sensory experiences but not cognitive experiences from the memory bank; a conscious mind knows knowing experiences, so freely selects these also from the memory bank. A self-conscious mind knows the structure of mind which is the set of invariant causal relations between cognitive experiences; so it can consciously express not only cognition but deductive reasoning. This accounts for the great advance in evolution made by Homo sapiens. The deductive reasoning was however confined to contingent knowledge until mathematics was discovered.

The reason why neuroscientists (Lashley, for example) cannot find memory traces in the brain, is because memory does not exist spatially but temporally. Feelings cause feelings, since consciousness, created by protein interactions, causes consciousness created by DNA interactions. The life of a cell is a set of feelings and its structure is a set of invariant (under GCT) causal relations between feelings. A cell does not have to know quantum theory in order to do this any more than non-living matter which also obeys quantum theory. An experience of feeling is identified by its consciousness, which is a set of invariant (under GCT) time-ordered acausal or causal relations between supramacromolecular protein or DNA interactions which violate CPT.

Causation is always in the direction C, P, T →C or P. This direction is from protein to DNA.

Darwin's theory cannot explain the origin of any species. In his theory, a species cannot begin by saltation with a single individual (a "hopeful" monster). In our theory, it must begin with a single individual (though the same mutation may occur in numerous environments): a new phlylogenetic experience must begin as a new ontogenetic experience since ontogeny creates phylogeny. This is far more logically satisfying than Darwinian theory; many biologists have expressed the need for an ontogeny-based phylogeny. But Darwinism eliminates the organism and its ontogeny (development) as being of any importance in principle: we are merely robots, programmed by our selfish genes or, just as bad, by our memes. There can be no denying that Darwinists do often behave like robots, replete with their armoury of totem pole aphorisms, but they can't fool us, you can see they're really human after all by the furious, almost demented, anger they display against any of their tribe so misguided as to step out of line. Some writers who have given superb, insightful criticisms of Darwinism have been accused by Darwinists of being moronic or worse. Free will has no role in Darwinism, nor has law-governed determinism: Que serà serà in the Darwinists' not so free-for-all. They have solved the problem of free will: there ain't any; of determinism and predestination: there ain't any; of life and mind; there ain't any, so expel them from your mind. (They are slightly ambiguous as to whether we should expel them from the mind we have or the mind we don't have.) Social Darwinism and evolutionary psychology have the scarcely hidden agenda of eliminating any possibility of free will or consciousness entering science, at least not by the front door. They drain biology, the science of life, of anything to do with life and all you are left with is a Newtonian biological machine. Yet we rightly got angry with Descartes for saying a dog is just a machine. Darwinism goes further and says the dog's owner is also a machine. Some dogs, it is true, become like their owner, or should that be the other way round? The free will of an organism determines its ontogenetic evolution and the free will of organisms, co-operatively, determines phylogenetic evolution. Whenever there is a discontinuity in the level of consciousness, a new species is created. In the classification of the species of man, however pale it may make palaeontologists, the ultimate criterion for a new species is a discontinuity in cultural consciousness and not phrenological cranial bumps.

Darwinists have the gall to claim that theirs is the first theory to recognise individuality. This hollow sham must be exposed. Darwin's theory suffocates individuality, as the outrageously intolerant, anti-scientific behaviour of its proponents affirms, seducing the mind along falsely logical paths which paralyse thought. What we owe most to Dawkins is this: by removing the individual from the causal chain of evolution save, as he puts it, as a mere passive "vehicle" for the genes, he exposes like a raw nerve for all to see, the totally "computerized", robotic character of a lifeless evolutionary process that lacks any figment of credibility, save for consciousness deprived sleepwalkers such as Dennett, Eldredge and Gould, who will not see. Scientists do not really believe Darwinism, they are mesmerized or transfixed, put on hold by it, their reasoning process suffocated and stifled by its deadly embrace, the anaconda smile. For Darwinism, evolution is the evolution of robots by transforming us into robots. If you are so misguided as to think this is an exaggeration then the transformation is complete. Until 1970, the human mind was afraid to look long and hard into the Darwinist landscape of evolution for fear and dread of what it might see. Dawkins, with a superb feel for metaphor, tore aside the veil, confirming our worst fears, expressed by so many great philosophers and artists. Ecstatic, he was convinced he was looking at the ultimate evolutionary masterpiece, wholly unaware he was looking at a grotesquely distorted death mask misrepresentation of the original. Dawkins used to claim that the Darwinist theory is true, but with his increasing awareness, thanks to Gould, of the lack of, but necessity for, a theory knowledge, he has modified his claim to its being the best existing theory. This is so, since it has so far been the only existing theory. Its esteemed contender, the Lamarck hypothesis, was not logically developed into a theory. In the present theory, individuality is truly affirmed. It is the individual ontogeny which creates phylogeny. A striking example of this in human evolution, especially in religious, scientific and artistic experience, is the genius who asserts his or her individuality with a new phylogenetic cultural experience even at the risk of death. The genius or hero is not concerned, primarily, with survival, but with the maximization of life. This is a most resounding slap in the face for brain-dead Darwinism.

The resolution of the EPR paradox indicates the direction of a theory of life's origin. In the non-living world there are only invariant, never non-invariant, time ordered relations between causally related interactions when causation is communicated by particles. Such non-invariance does exist in the non-living world in the case of quantum entanglement, when causation is communicated by energy alone and not by particles (a particle organises energy). But in a prebiotic system, because of dual CPT violation, for the first time in evolution there are non-invariant as well as invariant time-ordered relations for causally related interactions, in the communication of particles also. Hence the pairing, say A-T, can be causally related, as well as the inverse time-ordering T-A (or C-G and G-C). These causal relations relate the limbs of the ladder of DNA. No less importantly, the inverse is also true; i.e. there are invariant as well as non-invariant time ordered relations between *non*-causally related interactions. This defines a favourable mutation, that is an experientially caused mutation, microscopically, as a set of such invariant relations. These acausal relations relate the steps of the ladder of DNA. These invariant time-ordered acausal relations constitute the "language" system, that is the coding system of the organism. The relations are known to be favourable because they maximize the life of the organism.

The origin of life cannot be discovered without the formation of macroscopic laws of prebiotic and biotic systems. Three of these five laws are laws of unilateral increase. These are: The entropy of a prebiotic system has a unilaterally increasing tendency towards unilateral increase; The life of a biotic system increases unilaterally; The entropy of a biotic system increases unilaterally. The other two are: A life always selects with the purpose of maximizing the life as a whole; The life of a biotic system is the sum of the lives of its experiences.

There are three biological "arrows" of time. Like the arrow for the isolated system they are all increases in organisation. The arrow for isolated systems is a consequence of CP and T violation; for biotic systems a consequence of dual CPT violation. With the former, interactions cause interactions. With the latter, "information" in the form of sets of invariant relations, cause sets of invariant relations i.e. supras cause supras and macros cause macros. Instead of interactions between things causing interactions between things, things cause things for the first time in evolution. (Philosophers have suggested that besides events causing events, things cause things.) A biotic system is a self-organising bio-computer in which the information capable of being processed increases unilaterally. The more information a system has, the greater the diversity of choice available to it and so the greater the ratio of introns to exons in the genome. Could there be life elsewhere in the universe not constructed from DNA or protein? Yes. The theory only requires that life be constructed, mathematically, by C, P and T violation together with C or P violation - the nature of the chemicals being irrelevant. The philosopher, John Searle is correct: there is something special about biotic "machines": consciousness can only be created from supra-macros and they can only be created by a co-evolution of

209

CPT violation of both kinds. Life on earth began, not with RNA, but with DNA and protein. Which came first, the protein chicken or the DNA egg! (sorry). Neither! They co-evolved with protein always giving the causal lead. It is this co-evolution which gives the prebiotic system an ever-increasing tendency towards unilateral increase of entropy. Protein always causally feeds information (in the form of different kinds of structure) to DNA, and DNA returns the favour by feeding back information to form primary protein structure. You scratch my DNA and I'll scratch your protein.

What is classical physics? Quantum physics. There is no other physics. So why does it appear so different, even the opposite of quantum physics? Why does it work? Classical physics is Hamlet without Hamlet, so it has not a ghost of a chance of working, unless that is, it cheats. It only works in a limiting sense. A truly reversible process lasts to infinity; a mechanical interaction, without heat exchange, does not exist. Classical theory only works in specially selected phenomena, selected by physicists, who tacitly agree to subscribe to the fiction that the world is perfectly symmetrical, dimensionally, in the equations which describe its motion. But physics is now a tiny bit pregnant with the asymmetric interaction of radioactivity and there is no turning back. (God never screams if he can whisper.) Remove all the asymmetry, nonlinearity and non-conservation (of energy and momentum) from physics and nothing can happen in the universe; no work, no heat exchange, no entropy change. Classical physics is what quantum physics reduces to when you can afford to pretend this is not so.

Kant made large strides towards a true theory of knowledge but, by regarding experiences of the universe as being "appearances", he forfeited any chance of creating a theory of knowledge. Husserl corrected this in the twentieth century by regarding consciousness, the subjective, as being real. It is real because, by a law of logic, it symbolises reality. But Husserl did not know how to distinguish or relate temporal, experiential consciousness, the structure of experience, and universal consciousness; that is consciousness as it exists spatially in the universe, independently of experience. In visual experience, for example, the former exists in time, the latter in space, so a creative act of identification is needed for experience to relate its consciousness, which exists in time only, to universal consciousness, which also exists in space.

What is reality and truth? What is knowledge and how is it acquired? The main questions of philosophy used to be considered purely philosophical questions but these are questions of logical and structural science. The logical concept of reality has been proven to be the base which supports the entire edifice of science. It precedes even the concept of truth, which is defined in terms of reality. The scientific process consists in making statements about the construction of the universe (including statements about the minds which make those statements). The logical question arises: Are the statements true? To define truth, you need something real with which to define it, since how will you know if the statement is really true? (see how the words real and true stick to one another like glue). But how will you know the truth of what you select as real since you have no prior concept of truth. To seek to define truth a price must be paid since the logical circle must be entered. This can only be done if reality is defined as preceding truth and therefore only knowable by faith. We cannot evolve beyond religious faith unless we embrace scientific faith. The concept of god is a logical concept which has served its scientific purpose to pave the way to a higher form of evolutionary consciousness in which the sciences are unified. The definition of reality is not, of course, reality itself but a proposition about reality which is assumed to symbolise the proposed absolute reality and therefore, by definition, to be true. Godel has proved that the truth of mathematics is based on faith. Since the language of science is mathematical, the truth of science too must be based on faith. The def-

inition of reality enables truth to be defined. The Godel theorem implies that truth, if it is to be defined, can only be so
in terms of a concept which is not part of the system for
which we require a definition of truth. If truth is not
defined, the confusing and demoralising paradoxes of
semantics and quantum theory cannot be resolved. This is
the only theory which resolves all these paradoxes. No
other theory grasps the nettle of the concept of reality. In
our view, if only for this reason, this makes our theory the
only *real* theory of knowledge (the pun is unintentional but
unavoidable). Physics must relate to the other sciences if
science is to evolve. We propose that this new ontology is
essential for this to occur. Einstein always knew that Bohr
and his adherents would one day be wakened from their
pillow of solipsism. Einstein's lasting legacy was his acute
and troubled awareness of this problem and his attempt to
resolve it in the EPR paradox. It would be folly, in the
extreme, to yield to the fashionable philosophy of Bohr and
ignore, or underestimate, this great philosophical contribution of so great a physicist as Einstein. Ironically, though
Einstein and Godel were close friends, neither could have
had the faintest realisation as they strolled together on the
campus at Princeton, that the answer to each other's major
problem (reality and the continuum hypothesis) is contained in a union of their theories. Einstein said: "God is raffiniert (subtle, shrewd, canny)." Perhaps one should add,
"and has a mischievous sense of humour."

THE AUTHOR

This book originated from my conviction in the early 1950's, as a physics student at Edinburgh University, that a revolution in physics was necessary. There was talk in those days of the need for a unification not only of physics but of all the sciences, but it got no further than talk. As the decades passed the difficulty of unifying physics alone became increasingly apparent, so much so that the prospect of unifying the sciences was abandoned. In recent years, the failure of the numerous theories of the unification of physics has become obvious. I concluded that this failure was a consequence of tunnel vision, of a lack of ambition on the part of physicists; they could only succeed if they attempted the far wider unification of all the sciences.

As a student I was uncomfortably aware that the Einstein paradox of the twins was complete hokum, though I would have been hard put to it to say why. Far worse than this I was dismayed to find that my university lecturers had annihilated the very foundation of science as I conceived it to be.

I felt a compulsion to have a philosophical understanding of what was meant by reality. I was as yet unaware of the existence of the EPR paradox. The paradox, though postulated in the 1930's was not yet taught in universities in the 1950's. I was therefore unaware that, with EPR, Einstein tackled the very problem in which I was most interested: the nature of reality.

In my mid 20's, I developed schizophrenia. This affliction determined the subsequent course of my life, though not in an unfavorable way as you might think. In fact, it was essential in allowing me the freedom to devote my entire life to meditating and reflecting on the foundations of science. Years spent in relative isolation, cut off from the mainstream of society, have enabled me to develop the theory of the universe presented in this book. Were it not for my schizophrenia I may have remained within the conventional scientific community and risked falling victim to a much more destructive affliction: that of conforming to the establishment and losing my individual voice (or voices as the case may be!).

INDEX